THE *Hilton* BEDSIDE BOOK

Volume Seven

VOLUME SEVEN

THE
Hilton
BEDSIDE
BOOK

A TREASURY OF *Entertaining Reading*
SELECTED EXCLUSIVELY
FOR THE GUESTS OF *Hilton hotels*

PUBLISHED BY *Hilton Hotels Corporation*

PUBLISHED BY

Hilton Hotels Corporation

THE CONRAD HILTON, CHICAGO, ILLINOIS 60605

PREFACE

For those quiet moments in your hotel room—before the start of the day's activities, between engagements, when you're ready for bed but not quite ready for sleep—we are pleased to offer these varied entertainments in good reading, *The Hilton Bedside Book*, Volume Seven.

We hope that the wide diversity of reading pleasure contained in this selection of fiction, prose, and poetry will echo the reading tastes of our guests, offering not everything for all of you, but something for each of you.

You can play the role of detective on several vital cases, and test your own ideas on human physiology against the findings of experts Montagu and Darling. There's the vicarious thrill of helping a tenderfoot fisherman try to land his first giant gamefish. And a nostalgic 1920's visit to America's most human humorist, Robert Benchley. You'll hear the wild cry of a prehistoric sea-monster, and the not so different sound of a steam locomotive in the reminiscences of a country boy's love affair with trains.

Straight or mixed, here are suspense, nostalgia, humor, and adventure; myth, history, poetry, and fantasy; prehistoric and present-day animals; places faraway in time and in space; rogues, reticent ladies, sportsmen, and scientists.

Browser or burrower, may you find enjoyment!

Conrad N. Hilton, Chairman   Barron Hilton, President
Hilton Hotels Corporation

Contents

Contents 9

JACK FINNEY

Contents of the
Dead Man's Pocket

AT THE LITTLE LIVING-ROOM DESK Tom Benecke rolled two sheets of flimsy and a heavier top sheet, carbon paper sandwiched between them, into his portable. *Interoffice Memo*, the top sheet was headed, and he typed tomorrow's date just below this; then he glanced at a creased yellow sheet, covered with his own handwriting, beside the typewriter. "Hot in here," he muttered to himself. Then, from the short hallway at his back, he heard the muffled clang of wire coat hangers in the bedroom closet, and at this reminder of what his wife was doing he thought: Hot, hell—guilty conscience.

He got up, shoving his hands into the back pockets of his gray wash slacks, stepped to the living-room window beside the desk and stood breathing on the glass, watching the expanding circlet of mist, staring down through the autumn night at Lexington Avenue, eleven stories below. He was a tall, lean, dark-haired young man in a pullover sweater, who looked as though he had played not football, probably, but basketball in college. Now he placed the heels of his hands against the top edge of the lower window frame and shoved upward. But as usual the window didn't budge, and he had to lower his hands and then shoot them hard upward to jolt the window open a few inches. He dusted his hands, muttering.

But still he didn't begin his work. He crossed the room to the hallway entrance and, leaning against the doorjamb, hands shoved into his back pockets again, he called, "Clare?" When his wife answered, he said, "Sure you don't mind going alone?"

"No." Her voice was muffled, and he knew her head and shoulders were in the bedroom closet. Then the tap of her high heels sounded on the wood floor and she appeared at the end of the little hallway, wearing a slip, both hands raised to one ear, clipping on an earring. She smiled at him—a slender, very pretty girl with light brown, almost blonde, hair—her prettiness emphasized by the pleasant nature that showed in her face. "It's just that I hate you to miss this movie; you wanted to see it too."

"Yeah, I know." He ran his fingers through his hair. "Got to get this done though."

She nodded, accepting this. Then, glancing at the desk across the living room, she said, "You work too much, though, Tom— and too hard."

He smiled, "You won't mind though, will you, when the money comes rolling in and I'm known as the Boy Wizard of Wholesale Groceries?"

"I guess not." She smiled and turned back toward the bedroom.

At his desk again, Tom lighted a cigarette; then a few moments later as Clare appeared, dressed and ready to leave, he set it on the rim of the ash tray. "Just after seven," she said. "I can make the beginning of the first feature."

He walked to the front-door closet to help her on with her coat. He kissed her then and, for an instant, holding her close, smelling the perfume she had used, he was tempted to go with her; it was not actually true that he had to work tonight, though he very much wanted to. This was his own project, unannounced as yet in his office, and it could be postponed. But then they won't see it till Monday, he thought once again, and if I give it to the boss tomorrow he might read it over the weekend . . . "Have a good time," he said aloud. He gave his wife a little swat and opened the door for her, feeling the air from the building hallway, smelling faintly of floor wax, stream gently past his face.

He watched her walk down the hall, flicked a hand in response as she waved, and then he started to close the door, but it resisted for a moment. As the door opening narrowed, the current of warm air from the hallway, channeled through this smaller opening now, suddenly rushed past him with accelerated force. Behind him he heard the slap of the window curtains against the wall and the sound of paper fluttering from his desk, and he had to push to close the door.

Turning, he saw a sheet of white paper drifting to the floor in a series of arcs, and another sheet, yellow, moving toward the window, caught in the dying current flowing through the narrow opening. As he watched, the paper struck the bottom edge of the window and hung there for an instant, plastered against the glass and wood. Then as the moving air stilled completely, the curtains swinging back from the wall to hang free again, he saw the yellow sheet drop to the window ledge and slide over out of sight.

He ran across the room, grasped the bottom edge of the window and tugged, staring through the glass. He saw the yellow sheet, dimly now in the darkness outside, lying on the ornamental ledge a yard below the window. Even as he watched, it was moving, scraping slowly along the ledge, pushed by the breeze that pressed steadily against the building wall. He heaved on the window with all his strength and it shot open with a bang, the window weight rattling in the casing. But the paper was past his reach and, leaning out into the night, he watched it scud steadily along the ledge to the south, half plastered against the building wall. Above the muffled sound of the street traffic far below, he could hear the dry scrape of its movement, like a leaf on the pavement.

The living room of the next apartment to the south projected a yard or more farther out toward the street than this one; because of this the Beneckes paid seven and a half dollars less rent than their neighbors. And now the yellow sheet, sliding along the stone ledge, nearly invisible in the night, was stopped by the projecting blank wall of the next apartment. It lay motionless, then, in the corner formed by the two walls—a good five yards away, pressed firmly against the ornate corner ornament of the ledge by the breeze that moved past Tom Benecke's face.

He knelt at the window and stared at the yellow paper for a full minute or more, waiting for it to move, to slide off the ledge and fall, hoping he could follow its course to the street, and then hurry down in the elevator and retrieve it. But it didn't move, and then he saw that the paper was caught firmly between a projection of the convoluted corner ornament and the ledge. He thought about the poker from the fireplace, then the broom, then the mop—discarding each thought as it occurred to him. There was nothing in the apartment long enough to reach that paper.

It was hard for him to understand that he actually had to abandon it—it was ridiculous—and he began to curse. Of all the papers on his desk, why did it have to be this one in particular! On four long Saturday afternoons he had stood in supermarkets counting the people who passed certain displays, and the results were scribbled on that yellow sheet. From stacks of trade publications, gone over page by page in snatched half hours at work and during evenings at home, he had copied facts, quotations, and figures onto that sheet. And he had carried it with him to the Public Library on Fifth Avenue, where he'd spent a dozen lunch hours and early evenings adding more. All were needed to support and lend authority to his idea for a new grocery-store display method; without them his idea was a mere opinion. And there they all lay, in his own improvised shorthand—countless hours of work—out there on the ledge.

For many seconds he believed he was going to abandon the yellow sheet, that there was nothing else to do. The work could be duplicated. But it would take two months, and the time to present this idea, damn it, was *now*, for use in the spring displays. He struck his fist on the window ledge. Then he shrugged. Even though his plan were adopted, he told himself, it wouldn't bring him a raise in pay—not immediately, anyway, or as a direct result.

It won't bring me a promotion either, he argued—not of itself.

But just the same, and he couldn't escape the thought, this and other independent projects, some already done and others planned for the future, would gradually mark him out from the score of other young men in his company. They were the way to change from a name on the payroll to a name in the minds of the company officials. They were the beginning of the long, long climb to where he was determined to be, at the very top. And he knew he was going out there in the darkness, after the yellow sheet fifteen feet beyond his reach.

By a kind of instinct, he instantly began making his intention acceptable to himself by laughing at it. The mental picture of himself sidling along the ledge outside was absurd—it was actually comical—and he smiled. He imagined himself describing it; it would make a good story at the office and, it occurred to him, would add a special interest and importance to his memorandum, which would do it no harm at all.

To simply go out and get his paper was an easy task—he could be back here with it in less than two minutes—and he knew he wasn't deceiving himself. The ledge, he saw, measuring it with his eye, was about as wide as the length of his shoe, and perfectly flat. And every fifth row of brick in the face of the building, he remembered—leaning out, he verified this—was indented half an inch, enough for the tips of his fingers, enough to maintain balance easily. It occurred to him that if this ledge and wall were only a yard aboveground—as he knelt at the window staring out, this thought was the final confirmation of his intention—he could move along the ledge indefinitely.

On a sudden impulse, he got to his feet, walked to the front closet and took out an old tweed jacket; it would be cold outside. He put it on and buttoned it as he crossed the room rapidly toward the open window. In the back of his mind he knew he'd better hurry and get this over with before he thought too much, and at the window he didn't allow himself to hesitate.

He swung a leg over the sill, then felt for and found the ledge a yard below the window with his foot. Gripping the bottom of the window frame very tightly and carefully, he slowly ducked his head under it, feeling on his face the sudden change from the warm air of the room to the chill outside. With infinite care he brought out his other leg, his mind concentrating on what he was doing. Then he slowly stood erect. Most of the putty, dried out and brittle, had dropped off the bottom edging of the window frame, he found, and the flat wooden edging provided a good gripping surface, a half inch or more deep, for the tips of his fingers.

Now, balanced easily and firmly, he stood on the ledge outside in the slight, chill breeze, eleven stories above the street, staring into his own lighted apartment, odd and different-seeming now.

First his right hand, then his left, he carefully shifted his finger-tip grip from the puttyless window edging to an indented row of bricks directly to his right. It was hard to take the first shuffling sideways step then—to make himself move—and the fear stirred in his stomach, but he did it, again by not allowing himself time to think. And now—with his chest, stomach, and the left side of his face pressed against the rough cold brick—his lighted apartment was suddenly gone, and it was much darker out here than he had thought.

Without pause he continued—right foot, left foot, right foot, left—his shoe soles shuffling and scraping along the rough stone, never lifting from it, fingers sliding along the exposed edging of brick. He moved on the balls of his feet, heels lifted slightly; the ledge was not quite as wide as he'd expected. But leaning slightly inward toward the face of the building and pressed against it, he could feel his balance firm and secure, and moving along the ledge was quite as easy as he had thought it would be. He could hear the buttons of his jacket scraping steadily along the rough bricks and feel them catch momentarily, tugging a little, at each mortared crack. He simply did not permit himself to look down, though the compulsion to do so never left him; nor did he allow himself actually to think. Mechanically—right foot, left foot, over and again—he shuffled along crabwise, watching the projecting wall ahead loom steadily closer. . . .

Then he reached it and, at the corner—he'd decided how he was going to pick up the paper—he lifted his right foot and placed it carefully on the ledge that ran along the projecting wall at a right angle to the ledge on which his other foot rested. And now, facing the building, he stood in the corner formed by the two walls, one foot on the ledging of each, a hand on the shoulder-high indentation of each wall. His forehead was pressed directly into the corner against the cold bricks, and now he carefully lowered first one hand, then the other, perhaps a foot farther down, to the next indentation in the rows of bricks.

Very slowly, sliding his forehead down the trough of the brick corner and bending his knees, he lowered his body toward the paper lying between his outstretched feet. Again he lowered his fingerholds another foot and bent his knees still more, thigh muscles taut, his forehead sliding and bumping down the brick V. Half squatting now, he dropped his left hand to the next indentation and then slowly reached with his right hand toward the paper between his feet.

He couldn't quite touch it, and his knees now were pressed against the wall; he could bend them no farther. But by ducking his head another inch lower, the top of his head now pressed against the bricks, he lowered his right shoulder and his fingers had the paper by a corner, pulling it loose. At the same instant he saw, between his legs and far below, Lexington Avenue stretched out for miles ahead.

He saw, in that instant, the Loew's theater sign, blocks ahead past Fiftieth Street; the miles of traffic signals, all green now; the lights of cars and street lamps; countless neon signs; and the moving black dots of people. And a violent instantaneous explosion of absolute terror roared through him. For a motionless instant he saw himself externally—bent practically double, balanced on this narrow ledge, nearly half his body projecting out above the street far below—and he began to tremble violently, panic flaring through his mind and muscles, and he felt the blood rush from the surface of his skin.

In the fractional moment before horror paralyzed him, as he stared between his legs at that terrible length of street far beneath him, a fragment of his mind raised his body in a spasmodic jerk to an upright position again, but so violently that his head scraped hard against the wall, bouncing off it, and his body swayed outward to the knife edge of balance, and he very nearly plunged backward and fell. Then he was leaning far into the corner again, squeezing and pushing into it, not only his face but his chest and stomach, his back arching; and his finger tips clung with all the pressure of his pulling arms to the shoulder-high half-inch indentation in the bricks.

He was more than trembling now; his whole body was racked with a violent shuddering beyond control, his eyes squeezed so tightly shut it was painful, though he was past awareness of that. His teeth were exposed in a frozen grimace, the strength draining like water from his knees and calves. It was extremely likely, he knew, that he would faint, to slump down along the wall, his face scraping, and then drop backward, a limp weight, out into nothing. And to save his life he concentrated on holding onto consciousness, drawing deliberate deep breaths of cold air into his lungs, fighting to keep his senses aware.

Then he knew that he would not faint, but he could not stop shaking nor open his eyes. He stood where he was, breathing deeply, trying to hold back the terror of the glimpse he had had of what lay below him; and he knew he had made a mistake in not making himself stare down at the street, getting used to it and accepting it, when he had first stepped out onto the ledge.

It was impossible to walk back. He simply could not do it. He couldn't bring himself to make the slightest movement. The strength was gone from his legs; his shivering hands—numb, cold and desperately rigid—had lost all deftness; his easy ability to move and balance was gone. Within a step or two, if he tried to move, he knew that he would stumble clumsily and fall.

Seconds passed, with the chill faint wind pressing the side of his face, and he could hear the toned-down volume of the street traffic far beneath him. Again and again it slowed and then stopped, almost to silence; then presently, even this high, he would hear the click of the traffic signals and the subdued roar of the cars starting up again. During a lull in the street sounds, he called out. Then he was shouting *"Help!"* so loudly it rasped his throat. But he felt the steady pressure of the wind, moving between his face and the blank wall, snatch up his cries as he uttered them, and he knew they must sound directionless and distant. And he remembered how habitually, here in New York, he himself heard and ignored shouts in the night. If anyone heard him, there was no sign of it, and presently Tom Benecke knew he had to try moving; there was nothing else he could do.

Eyes squeezed shut, he watched scenes in his mind like scraps of motion-picture film—he could not stop them. He saw himself stumbling suddenly sideways as he crept along the ledge and saw his upper body arc outward, arms flailing. He saw a dangling shoe-string caught between the ledge and the sole of his other shoe, saw a foot start to move, to be stopped with a jerk, and felt his balance leaving him. He saw himself falling, with a terrible speed as his body revolved in the air, knees clutched tight to his chest, eyes squeezed shut, moaning softly.

Out of utter necessity, knowing that any of these thoughts might be reality in the very next seconds, he was slowly able to shut his mind against every thought but what he now began to do. With fear-soaked slowness, he slid his left foot an inch or two toward his own impossibly distant window. Then he slid the fingers of his shivering left hand a corresponding distance. For a moment he could not bring himself to lift his right foot from one ledge to the other; then he did it, and became aware of the harsh exhalation of air from his throat and realized that he was panting. As his right hand, then, began to slide along the brick edging, he was astonished to feel the yellow paper pressed to the bricks underneath his stiff fingers, and he uttered a terrible, abrupt bark that might have been a laugh or a moan. He opened his mouth and took the paper in his teeth, pulling it out from under his fingers.

By a kind of trick—by concentrating his entire mind on first his left foot, then his left hand, then the other foot, then the other hand—he was able to move, almost imperceptibly, trembling steadily, very nearly without thought. But he could feel the terrible strength of the pent-up horror on just the other side of the flimsy barrier he had erected in his mind; and he knew that if it broke through he would lose this thin artificial control of his body.

During one slow step he tried keeping his eyes closed; it made him feel safer, shutting him off a little from the fearful reality of where he was. Then a sudden rush of giddiness swept over him and he had to open his eyes wide, staring sideways at the cold rough brick and angled lines of mortar, his cheek tight against the building. He kept his eyes open then, knowing that if he once let them flick outward, to stare for an instant at the lighted windows across the street, he would be past help.

He didn't know how many dozens of tiny sidling steps he had taken, his chest, belly and face pressed to the wall; but he knew the slender hold he was keeping on his mind and body was going to break. He had a sudden mental picture of his apartment on just the other side of this wall—warm, cheerful, incredibly spacious. And he saw himself striding through it, lying down on the floor on his back, arms spread wide, reveling in its unbelievable security. The impossible remoteness of this utter safety, the contrast between it and where he now stood, was more than he could bear. And the barrier broke then, and the fear of the awful height he stood on coursed through his nerves and muscles.

A fraction of his mind knew he was going to fall, and he began taking rapid blind steps with no feeling of what he was doing, sidling with a clumsy desperate swiftness, fingers scrabbling along the brick, almost hopelessly resigned to the sudden backward pull and swift motion outward and down. Then his moving left hand slid onto not brick but sheer emptiness, an impossible gap in the face of the wall, and he stumbled.

His right foot smashed into his left anklebone; he staggered sideways, began falling, and the claw of his hand cracked against glass and wood, slid down it, and his finger tips were pressed hard on the puttyless edging of his window. His right hand smacked gropingly beside it as he fell to his knees; and, under the full weight and direct downward pull of his sagging body, the open window dropped shudderingly in its frame till it closed and his wrists struck the sill and were jarred off.

For a single moment he knelt, knee bones against stone on the very edge of the ledge, body swaying and touching nowhere else, fighting for balance. Then he lost it, his shoulders plunging backward, and he flung his arms forward, his hands smashing against the window casing on either side; and—his body moving backward—his fingers clutched the narrow wood stripping of the upper pane.

For an instant he hung suspended between balance and falling, his finger tips pressed onto the quarter-inch wood strips. Then, with utmost delicacy, with a focused concentration of all his senses, he increased even further the strain on his finger tips hooked to these slim edgings of wood. Elbows slowly bending, he began to draw the full weight of his upper body forward, knowing that the instant his fingers slipped off these quarter-inch strips he'd plunge backward and be falling. Elbows imperceptibly bending, body shaking with the strain, the sweat starting from his forehead in great sudden drops, he pulled, his entire being and thought concentrated in his finger tips. Then suddenly, the strain slackened and ended, his chest touching the window sill, and he was kneeling on the ledge, his forehead pressed to the glass of the closed window.

Dropping his palms to the sill, he stared into his living room— at the red-brown davenport across the room, and a magazine he had left there; at the pictures on the walls, and the gray rug; the entrance to the hallway; and at his papers, typewriter, and desk, not two feet from his nose. A movement from his desk caught his eye and he saw that it was a thin curl of blue smoke; his cigarette, the ash long, was still burning in the ash tray where he'd left it—this was past all belief—only a few minutes before.

His head moved, and in faint reflection from the glass before him he saw the yellow paper clenched in his front teeth. Lifting a hand from the sill he took it from his mouth; the moistened corner parted from the paper, and he spat it out.

For a moment, in the light from the living room, he stared wonderingly at the yellow sheet in his hand and then crushed it into the side pocket of his jacket.

He couldn't open the window. It had been pulled not completely closed, but its lower edge was below the level of the outside sill; there was no room to get his fingers underneath it. Between the upper sash and the lower was a gap not wide enough—reaching up, he tried—to get his fingers into; he couldn't push it open. The upper window panel, he knew from long experience, was impossible to move, frozen tight with dried paint.

Very carefully observing his balance, the finger tips of his left hand again hooked to the narrow stripping of the window casing, he drew back his right hand, palm facing the glass, and then struck the glass with the heel of his hand.

His arm rebounded from the pane, his body tottering, and he knew he didn't dare strike a harder blow.

But in the security and relief of his new position, he simply smiled; with only a sheet of glass between him and the room just before him, it was not possible that there wasn't a way past it. Eyes narrowing, he thought for a few moments about what to do. Then his eyes widened, for nothing occurred to him. But still he felt calm: the trembling, he realized, had stopped. At the back of his mind there still lay the thought that once he was again in his home, he could give release to his feelings. He actually *would* lie on the floor, rolling, clenching tufts of the rug in his hands. He would literally run across the room, free to move as he liked, jumping on the floor, testing and reveling in its absolute security, letting the relief flood through him, draining the fear from his mind and body. His yearning for this was astonishingly intense, and somehow he understood that he had better keep this feeling at bay.

He took a half dollar from his pocket and struck it against the pane, but without any hope that the glass would break and with very little disappointment when it did not. After a few moments of thought he drew his leg up onto the ledge and picked loose the knot of his shoelace. He slipped off the shoe and, holding it across the instep, drew back his arm as far as he dared and struck the leather heel against the glass. The pane rattled, but he knew he'd been a long way from breaking it. His foot was cold and he slipped the shoe back on. He shouted again, experimentally, and then once more, but there was no answer.

The realization suddenly struck him that he might have to wait here till Clare came home, and for a moment the thought was funny. He could see Clare opening the front door, withdrawing her key from the lock, closing the door behind her, and then glancing up to see him crouched on the other side of the window. He could see her rush across the room, face astounded and frightened, and hear himself shouting instructions: "Never mind how I got here! Just open the wind—" She couldn't open it, he remembered, she'd never been able to; she'd always had to call him. She'd have to get the building superintendent or a neighbor, and he pictured himself smiling and answering their questions as he climbed in. "I just wanted to get a breath of fresh air, so—"

He couldn't possibly wait here till Clare came home. It was the second feature she'd wanted to see, and she'd left in time to see the first. She'd be another three hours or— He glanced at his watch; Clare had been gone eight minutes. It wasn't possible, but only eight minutes ago he had kissed his wife good-by. She wasn't even at the theater yet!

It would be four hours before she could possibly be home, and he tried to picture himself kneeling out here, finger tips hooked to these narrow strippings, while first one movie, preceded by a slow listing of credits, began, developed, reached its climax, and then finally ended. There'd be a newsreel next, maybe, and then an animated cartoon, and then interminable scenes from coming pictures. And then, once more, the beginning of a full-length picture —while all the time he hung out here in the night.

He might possibly get to his feet, but he was afraid to try. Already his legs were cramped, his thigh muscles tired; his knees hurt, his feet felt numb, and his hands were stiff. He couldn't possibly stay out here for four hours, or anywhere near it. Long before that his legs and arms would give out; he would be forced to try changing his position often—stiffly, clumsily, his co-ordination and strength gone—and he would fall. Quite realistically, he knew that he would fall; no one could stay out here on this ledge for four hours.

A dozen windows in the apartment building across the street were lighted. Looking over his shoulder, he could see the top of a man's head behind the newspaper he was reading; in another window he saw the blue-gray flicker of a television screen. No more than twenty-odd yards from his back were scores of people, and if just one of them would walk idly to his window and glance out. . . . For some moments he stared over his shoulder at the lighted rectangles, waiting. But no one appeared. The man reading his paper turned a page and then continued his reading. A figure passed another of the windows and was immediately gone.

In the inside pocket of his jacket he found a little sheaf of papers, and he pulled one out and looked at it in the light from the living room. It was an old letter, an advertisement of some sort; his name and address, in purple ink, were on a label pasted to the envelope. Gripping one end of the envelope in his teeth, he twisted it into a tight curl. From his shirt pocket he brought out a book of matches. He didn't dare let go the casing with both hands but, with the twist of paper in his teeth, he opened the matchbook with his free hand; then he bent one of the matches in two without tearing it from the folder, its red-tipped end now touching the striking surface. With his thumb, he rubbed the red tip across the striking area.

He did it again, then again, and still again, pressing harder each time, and the match suddenly flared, burning his thumb. But he kept it alight, cupping the matchbook in his hand and shielding it with his body. He held the flame to the paper in his mouth till it caught. Then he snuffed out the match flame with his thumb and forefinger, careless of the burn, and replaced the book in his pocket. Taking the paper twist in his hand, he held it flame down, watching the flame crawl up the paper, till it flared bright. Then he held it behind him over the street, moving it from side to side, watching it over his shoulder, the flame flickering and guttering in the wind.

There were three letters in his pocket and he lighted each of them, holding each till the flame touched his hand, then dropping it to the street below. At one point, watching over his shoulder while the last of the letters burned, he saw the man across the street put down his paper and stand—even seeming, to Tom, to glance toward his window. But when he moved, it was only to walk across the room and disappear from sight.

There were a dozen coins in Tom Benecke's pocket and he dropped them, three or four at a time. But if they struck anyone, or if anyone noticed their falling, no one connected them with their source, and no one glanced upward.

His arms had begun to tremble from the steady strain of clinging to this narrow perch, and he did not know what to do now and was terribly frightened. Clinging to the window stripping with one hand, he again searched his pockets. But now—he had left his wallet on his dresser when he'd changed clothes—there was nothing left but the yellow sheet. It occurred to him irrelevantly that his death on the sidewalk below would be an eternal mystery; the window closed—why, how, and from where could he have fallen? No one would be able to identify his body for a time, either—the thought was somehow unbearable and increased his fear. All they'd find in his pockets would be the yellow sheet. *Contents of the dead man's pockets,* he thought, *one sheet of paper bearing penciled notations—incomprehensible.*

He understood fully that he might actually be going to die; his arms, maintaining his balance on the ledge, were trembling steadily now. And it occurred to him then with all the force of a revelation that, if he fell, all he was ever going to have out of life he would then, abruptly, have had. Nothing, then, could ever be changed; and nothing more—no least experience or pleasure—could ever be added to his life. He wished, then, that he had not allowed his wife to go off by herself tonight—and on similar nights. He thought of all the evenings he had spent away from her, working; and he regretted them. He thought wonderingly of his fierce ambition and of the direction his life had taken; he thought of the hours he'd spent by himself, filling the yellow sheet that had brought him out here. *Contents of the dead man's pockets,* he thought with sudden fierce anger, *a wasted life.*

He was simply not going to cling here till he slipped and fell; he told himself that now. There was one last thing he could try; he had been aware of it for some moments, refusing to think about it, but now he faced it. Kneeling here on the ledge, the finger tips of one hand pressed to the narrow strip of wood, he could, he knew, draw his other hand back a yard perhaps, fist clenched tight, doing it very slowly till he sensed the outer limit of balance, then, as hard as he was able from the distance, he could drive his fist forward against the glass. If it broke, his fist smashing through, he was safe; he might cut himself badly, and probably would, but with his arm inside the room he would be secure. But if the glass did not break, the rebound, flinging his arm back, would topple him off the ledge. He was certain of that.

He tested his plan. The fingers of his left hand clawlike on the little stripping, he drew back his other fist until his body began teetering backward. But he had no leverage now—he could feel that there would be no force to his swing—and he moved his fist slowly forward till he rocked forward on his knees again and could sense that his swing would carry its greatest force. Glancing down, however, measuring the distance from his fist to the glass, he saw that it was less than two feet.

It occurred to him that he could raise his arm over his head, to bring it down against the glass. But, experimenting in slow motion, he knew it would be an awkward girl-like blow without the force of a driving punch, and not nearly enough to break the glass.

Facing the window, he had to drive a blow from the shoulder, he knew now, at a distance of less than two feet; and he did not know whether it would break through the heavy glass. It might; he could picture it happening, he could feel it in the nerves of his arm. And it might not; he could feel that too—feel his fist striking this glass and being instantaneously flung back by the unbreaking pane, feel the fingers of his other hand breaking loose, nails scraping along the casing as he fell.

He waited, arm drawn back, fist balled, but in no hurry to strike; this pause, he knew, might be an extension of his life. And to live even a few seconds longer, he felt, even out here on this ledge in the night, was infinitely better than to die a moment earlier than he had to. His arm grew tired, and he brought it down and rested it.

Then he knew that it was time to make the attempt. He could not kneel here hesitating indefinitely till he lost all courage to act, waiting till he slipped off the ledge. Again he drew back his arm, knowing this time that he would not bring it down till he struck. His elbow protruding over Lexington Avenue far below, the fingers of his other hand pressed down bloodlessly tight against the narrow stripping, he waited, feeling the sick tenseness and terrible excitement building. It grew and swelled toward the moment of action, his nerves tautening. He thought of Clare—just a wordless, yearning thought—and then drew his arm back just a bit more, fist so tight his fingers pained him, and knowing he was going to do it. Then with full power, with every last scrap of strength he could bring to bear, he shot his arm forward toward the glass, and he said, *"Clare!"*

He heard the sound, felt the blow, felt himself falling forward, and his hand closed on the living-room curtains, the shards and fragments of glass showering onto the floor. And then, kneeling there on the ledge, an arm thrust into the room up to the shoulder, he began picking away the protruding slivers and great wedges of glass from the window frame, tossing them in onto the rug. And, as he grasped the edges of the empty window frame and climbed into his home, he was grinning in triumph.

He did not lie down on the floor or run through the apartment, as he had promised himself; even in the first few moments it seemed to him natural and normal that he should be where he was. He simply turned to his desk, pulled the crumpled yellow sheet from his pocket and laid it down where it had been, smoothing it out; then he absently laid a pencil across it to weight it down. He shook his head wonderingly, and turned to walk toward the closet.

There he got out his topcoat and hat and, without waiting to put them on, opened the front door and stepped out, to go find his wife. He turned to pull the door closed and the warm air from the hall rushed through the narrow opening again. As he saw the yellow paper, the pencil flying, scooped off the desk and, unimpeded by the glassless window, sail out into the night and out of his life, Tom Benecke burst into laughter and then closed the door behind him.

COREY FORD

The Best Years of Life

Life TODAY IS A COLOSSAL ENTERPRISE, with a world-wide staff running into the thousands and sumptuous home offices sprawled over five floors of the glass-and-steel Time-Life Building. Nothing remains of the former magazine which Henry Luce purchased in 1936 except its name; but a few diehards still remember with affection the old *Life*—the short but merry one—which was the leading humor magazine of the early Twenties.

Its staff numbered barely a dozen, and its modest editorial sanctum took up half of one floor in an anonymous office building at 598 Madison Avenue. A hopeful contributor would step from the elevator into a drab reception hall, hung with Maxfield Parrish originals and dominated by an enormous stained-glass rendition of the traditional editorial page drawing—a mounted knight, his shield labeled LIFE and his pen leveled like a lance, pursuing a bat-winged devil across the landscape—which had decorated every issue since the first in 1883. The receptionist's desk was usually vacant, and after shifting uncertainly from one foot to the other the visitor would push open a door marked "Editorial" and enter timidly, his precious manuscript or cartoon in hand.

And I would give all the glossy issues of Mr. Luce's *Life* to enter that door again, to breathe the familiar musty odor of cigarette smoke and printer's ink and paste, to hear the clacking typewriters and an occasional bellow from the region of the art department, to catch a glimpse of Bob Sherwood's lanky figure towering above the half-partition which fenced off the editor's private lair. The all too small office space was subdivided into smaller cubicles, desks were piled high with manuscripts and exchange magazines, everything was as cluttered and happy as a child's playroom.

Life was entering its best years. Charles Dana Gibson had bought it in 1920, and Robert E. Sherwood, who was promoted to editor in 1924, was rapidly lifting it out of its stodgy middle-aged rut. Gibson was as square-jawed and austere as the bust of a Roman senator; he had married one of the beautiful Langhorne sisters of Virginia, and used her as model for the famous Gibson Girl he created in the Nineties. He took no interest in the problems of advertising and circulation, and preferred to sit at his drawing board sketching a center spread for the next issue. The direction of the magazine was left to Sherwood and the art editor, bald pipe-smoking Frank Casey, whose bland Irish smile could assuage the pain of a refusal. Casey hovered over his brood of artists like a motherly hen, and there were always two or three noted illustrators perched on radiators or stacks of books in his cramped office: James Montgomery Flagg, or Ellison Hoover, or Tony Sarg, or Reginald Birch, or the white-bearded patriarchal T. S. Sullivant, or Percy Crosby, whose tough little gamin had just been christened Skippy and made a regular cartoon feature.

Sherwood was an immensely sympathetic and friendly man, slow-spoken, somber in appearance, and somewhat shy. In addition to his duties as editor, he wrote a weekly column of movie reviews, illuminated by such pungent observations as his comment on Tom Mix: "They say he rides like part of the horse, but they don't say which part." He was particularly sensitive about his spectacular height of six feet seven inches, which was the subject of endless japes by his friends. Asked at a party how well he knew Sherwood, Robert Benchley climbed onto a chair, extended his arm aloft to its full reach, and replied, "Why, I've known him since he was *this* high." And when Sherwood missed several lunches at the Algonquin Round Table because of illness, Dorothy Parker wired him: WE'VE TURNED DOWN A VACANT STEPLADDER FOR YOU.

Veteran member of *Life*'s staff when I arrived on the scene was Oliver Herford, who had written for the magazine since its first issue and whose barbed wit had strewn its pages with victims over the years. He was a figure of fantasy, short and wispy and as gray as lint: disordered gray hair, an ill-fitting gray suit, pearl-gray spats, a monocle on a long faded ribbon. (Someone asked him once why his suits were always the same color. "Saves me a world of trouble," Herford answered. "When spring comes around, I merely write my tailor, send him a small sample of dandruff, and tell him to match it exactly.") He showed up one day wearing an outrageous gray derby, and explained that it was a whim of his wife's. Friends advised him to throw it away. "Ah, but you don't know my wife," he sighed. "She has a whim of iron."

In addition to the staff writers, Sherwood had lured to *Life* such stellar contributors as Ring Lardner, Marc Connelly, Mrs. Parker, and the incomparable Mr. Benchley, whose ready laugh filled the magazine's dingy office with sunshine. Benchley's unique gift was his ability to listen, to grin in eager anticipation as you talked, to acknowledge your banal joke with a flattering guffaw. "It doesn't matter what your yarn happens to be, or how old or how shopworn," F.P.A. commented. "Benchley will burst into laughter, and you will go away thinking that you must be a witty dog." None of his quips had the faintest tinge of malice; I don't think Bob Benchley had an enemy in the world. "Everybody wanted to be his close friend, and to be with him all the time," Frank Sullivan wrote in his introduction to a posthumous collection of Benchley's articles, "and he, kindly and gregarious man that he was, would have liked to oblige. But there simply was not enough Benchley to go around."

No other humorist, with the exception of Sullivan himself, has ever been so idolized as a craftsman, so universally loved by everyone who knew him. It must have puzzled Benchley to see a twenty-one-year-old hanging around the *Life* office, but he went out of his way to be kind to me. When I started writing regularly for the magazine in 1923, I faced what was to me a serious problem. Another writer named, by wild coincidence, Torrey Ford was contributing pieces at the same time; and I asked Mr. Benchley how to avoid confusion. He pondered a moment. "You could print your own stuff in a different color ink," he suggested gravely, "but that might run into expense. Maybe the best idea would be to let Torrey handle the articles, and you handle the checks."

The building in which *Life* was located stood on the northwest corner of Madison and Fifty-ninth Street. A bank occupied the ground floor (have you ever heard of a bank on the second floor, by the way?) with a burly uniformed guard at the entrance; and Mr. Benchley, on his way to the office, had to run the gauntlet of the guard's suspicious gaze. Benchley was one of those timid souls who invariably look guilty whenever they encounter someone in uniform, whether policeman or bus driver or even Western Union messenger; but he felt that this daily scrutiny called for some overt act. Emerging from the building one afternoon, he loitered at the corner and glanced furtively up and down the street until he caught the attention of the scowling guard. In his stealthiest manner, he tore a page from his newspaper, crumpled it into a ball, knelt, and placed it against the marble side of the bank. The guard's scowl deepened and he took a menacing step forward. Hastily Benchley struck a match, lit the paper, and bolted around the corner and down Fifty-ninth Street out of sight.

Banks and Benchley never got along very well together. His persistent habit of overdrawing his account led to a certain coolness in their relationship, and staid bankers were baffled by the gay little messages he wrote when he endorsed the back of a check: "Dear Banker's Trust, I love you. Bob" or "Having wonderful time, wish you were here. Robert Rabbit Benchley." Once, when living in Crestwood, he asked his local bank for a loan, and it was given to him without question. After brooding about it overnight, he withdrew all his savings in the morning. "I don't trust a bank," he explained, "that would lend money to such a poor risk."

His casual attitude toward money was a matter of concern to all his friends. Despite the lucrative earnings from his humor articles, his radio and theater engagements, and later his phenomenally successful movie shorts—*How to Sleep* won the Academy Award for 1936—he was never quite solvent. Chance acquaintances were always hitting him up for something to tide them over, he was a ready sucker for any hard-luck story along Broadway, and he had an irresistible compulsion to grab every restaurant check and bar tab. When Irving Berlin hired him to deliver his "Treasurer's Report" at the Music Box Revue, he earned five hundred dollars a week during the show's nine-month run; but after it closed he had to ask *Life* for a month's advance salary to pay his debts.

Not that he ever regretted a penny he squandered. "I am known as a bad business man from one end of the country to just a little beyond the same end," he wrote of himself frankly in 1930. "Of course, if I wanted to, I might point out that out of a possible $5,000 which I have made since I left school I have had $3,000 worth of good food (all of which has gone into making bone and muscle and some nice fat), $1,500 worth of theater tickets, and $500 worth of candy; whereas many of my business friends have simply had $5,000 worth of whatever that stock was which got so yellow along about last November."

Robert Benchley looked precisely as Gluyas Williams drew him. A master artist, whose deft pen-strokes caught the plaintive and frustrated character of his subject, Williams illustrated every one of Benchley's books, and their collaboration was made in heaven. The familiar Williams portrait—round bewildered face, toothbrush mustache, a figure that tended to bulge in odd places—became Benchley's public image, and readers could visualize the dapper boulevardier whose dress shirt insisted on buckling, the hapless victim of his own bumbling inefficiency, and identify themselves with him in his bewilderment.

Since most of Benchley's articles were written in the first person, with himself the butt of his own jokes, he remains the best authority on his appearance, a subject on which he dwelt frequently. "This does not mean I am *pleased* with it, mind you, or that I can even tolerate it," he noted in an essay entitled "My Face." "I simply have a morbid interest in it." His trouble, he conceded, was that he never knew whom he would resemble in the morning until he glanced at his reflection in the mirror.

One day I look like Wimpy, the hamburger fancier in the Popeye the Sailor saga. Another day it may be Wallace Beery. And a third day, if I have let my moustache get out of hand, it is Bairnsfather's Old Bill. Some mornings, if I look in the mirror soon enough after getting out of bed, there is no resemblance to any character at all, either in or out of fiction, and I turn quickly to look behind me, convinced that a stranger has spent the night with me and is peering over my shoulder in a sinister fashion, merely to frighten me. On such occasions, the shock of finding that I am actually the possessor of the face in the mirror is sufficient to send me scurrying back to bed, completely unnerved.

Mirrors were a perpetual source of chagrin to Benchley, and he tried not to look into them any more than was absolutely necessary. "Things are depressing enough as they are," he confessed in "Malignant Mirrors," "without my going out of my way to make myself miserable." He found this particularly true when trying on a hat.

I have never seen a meaner face than mine in the hat-store mirror. I could stand its not being handsome, I could even stand looking weak in an attractive, man-about-town sort of way. But in the right-hand mirror there confronts me a hang-dog face, the face of a yellow craven, while at the left leers an even more repulsive type, sensual and cruel. Furthermore, even though I have had a haircut that very day, there is an unkempt fringe showing over my collar in back, and the collar itself (a Wimpet, 14½, which looked so well on the young man in the carcard) seems to be something which would be worn by a Maine guide when he goes into Portland for the day. My suit needs pressing and there is a general air of its having been given to me, with ten dollars, by the State on my departure from Sing Sing the day before.

Benchley lived his life in a constant state of humiliation, the prey of shoelaces that broke at inconvenient moments, fountain pens that refused to write, or military brushes that would fly out of his hands, execute a takeoff of perhaps a foot and a half, and then crash onto his forehead. "I have placed slippers very carefully under my bed," he complained, "only to have them crawl out during the night to a position where I will step into them the wrong way round when leaping out of bed to answer the telephone." He saw it as a deliberate campaign against him by the inanimate underworld. "These things don't just happen, you know. They are proofs of a very clear conspiracy to hurt me physically, which exists among household objects, and against which I have no defense. All that I can do is to walk around all day crouched over with one elbow raised to ward off the heavier attacks which are being aimed at me. This gives a man a cringing look which becomes a personal characteristic."

Although Benchley has been hailed as America's greatest humorist of the century— "He wrote some of the funniest things ever written by an American," Marc Connelly stated, and Stephen Leacock agreed: "As a writer of nonsense for nonsense' sake, he is unsurpassed"—Benchley held his talents in low esteem. "It took me all these years to find I had no gift for writing," he confided to Connelly once. If someone complimented him on his style, he would protest, "I don't know enough words to have a style. I know, at the most, fifteen adjectives." He looked on himself as an amateur; and that may account for his lack of affectation, the essentially modest quality of his work.

His style was deceptively easy, but I hate to contemplate the number of embryo humorists who have come a cropper trying to imitate it. He would disarm the reader with an offhand opening paragraph: "Two or three fishermen have written in asking this department if it believes that dreams go by opposites. I am still trying to tie up their question in some way with fishing, but I can't quite figure it out. I don't even know that they were fishermen." Sometimes he would double back on his tracks and contradict his whole premise. "A great many people have come up to me and asked me how I manage to get so much work done and still keep looking so dissipated. My answer is 'Don't you wish you knew?' and a pretty good answer it is, too, when you consider that nine times out of ten I didn't hear the original question."

Benchley himself defined humor as "anything that makes anybody laugh. Personally I like humor that has extravagance, a mad quality." This quality of madness—what Joseph Bryan III has called "his dislocated logic, his combination of nonsense and *non sequitur*"—puts him in a class with Lardner or Lear or Lewis Carroll. He had a sure ear for the absurd, as shown in his names for flowers—"double-gaited wertroot" and "Walmsley's cowlick" and "Crazy Kitty, or MacNerty's fields-awash"—or his description of a woman's dream (Case B) in "Do Dreams Go by Opposites?":

In her dream she was in a greenhouse full of exotic plants, which was on a sort of funicular, running up and down the side of a mountain. The mountain was just a shade narrower than the greenhouse, so the ends of the greenhouse jutted out on either side, making it difficult for automobile traffic, which was very heavy at this point, to pass. In the greenhouse with the woman was a deaf elk which had got in somehow through a hole in the screen. The elk couldn't hear a word that the woman was saying, so she just went on with her tapestry-weaving, as she had to have the job finished before the greenhouse got to the top of the mountain on its 11 o'clock trip. (That is, 11 o'clock from the foot of East Fourteenth Street, where it started.)

Nor could anyone else but Benchley have written:

A dog teaches a boy fidelity, perseverance and to turn around three times before lying down.

Here the matter stands, or rather *there* (it was here a minute ago).

The rooster is an entirely different sort of bird from the hen. He is very proud and has a red crest on top of his head. This red crest is put there by Nature so that the hen can see the rooster coming in a crowd and can hop into a taxi or make a previous engagement if she

wants to. A favorite dodge of a lot of hens when they see the red crest
of the rooster making in their direction across the barnyard is to work
up a sick headache. One of the happiest and most contented roosters
I ever saw was one who had had his red crest chewed off in a fight
with a dog. He also wore sneakers.

Probably the best known of all Benchley classics is his 1,185-
word monologue called "The Treasurer's Report." Benchley is said
to have composed it in eight and a half minutes on his way down-
town in a taxi (considerably less time than Lincoln required for
his "Gettysburg Address") and delivered it at an amateur revue
put on by the group of artists and writers who lunched regularly
at the Algonquin. The show was called *No, Siree!*, after the current hit *Chauve-Souris*, and it opened—and closed—on April 30,
1922. Benchley's skit was not listed on the program, and few of
the fashionable audience knew him when he walked on stage, unannounced, and began apologetically: "I shall take but a very few
minutes of your time this evening, for I realize that you would
much rather be listening to this interesting entertainment than to
a dry financial statement."

Some of the audience glanced at their watches and looked toward the exits, and one or two at the rear of the theater left their
seats and started up the aisle.

"But I *am* reminded of a story—which you have probably all of
you heard," Benchley floundered. "It seems there were two Irish-
men walking down the street when they came to a—Oh, I should
have said in the first place that the parrot which was hanging out
in *front* of the store—or rather belonging to one of these two fellows—the *first* Irishman, that is—was—well, *any*way, this parrot—"

There was a snicker in the audience, a sudden snort, a rising
crescendo of laughter as it dawned on his listeners that this was a
parody of the sincere but inept public speaker, caught up in the
spell of his own oratory. Realizing that his story was as good as
lost, Benchley abandoned it and stepped forward with a brisk busi-
nesslike air.

"Now, in connection with reading this report, there are one or two points which Dr. Murnie wanted brought up in connection with it, and he has asked me to bring them up in connec—to bring them up." Benchley made a nervous attempt to straighten his black bow tie. "In the first place, there is the question of the work which we are trying to do up there at our little place at Silver Lake, a work which we feel not only fills a very definite need in the community but also fills a very definite need—er—in the community." He gave another tug at his bow tie, which came undone. "For instance, I don't think it is generally known that most of our boys are between the age of fourteen."

The laughter had built to a steady roar, the members of the audience were doubled over holding their sides and gasping for breath, and by the time Benchley exited, bumping into the proscenium, he had already won his niche in the humorists' hall of fame.

Benchley never wanted to be known as a humorist. When he graduated from Harvard in 1912, where he earned a considerable reputation for comedy as president of the *Lampoon,* he resolved, "I'm not going to be a funny man all my life." Nathaniel Benchley, in his affectionate biography of his father, states that Benchley's private ambitions were to be a social-service worker, and to write a history of Queen Anne. Up to the time of his death, he was still collecting books on the Queen Anne period to use in the research for his magnum opus.

After college Benchley ran swiftly through a series of jobs, ranging from a brief stint organizing clambakes for the employees of a Boston paper company—"I've never looked a clam in the face since," he observed—to an even briefer engagement with the advertising department of the Curtis Publishing Company in Philadelphia. Their association terminated abruptly when Benchley, dressed in a red wig and matching beard and posing as the president of a nonexistent Seattle advertising agency, delivered a lengthy diatribe against the Curtis Publishing Company at their annual banquet. He recalled later: "When I left Curtis (I was given plenty of time to get my hat and coat) I was advised not to stick to advertising. They said I was too tall, or something. I forget just what the reason was they gave." Starvation was narrowly averted when Frank Crowninshield, editor of the elite *Vanity Fair,* hired him as its managing editor at the munificent stipend of a hundred dollars a week.

Here he formed two enduring friendships: Mrs. Dorothy Parker, a demure little lady with the tongue of an adder, who was *Vanity Fair's* drama critic, and a long lean veteran of the Canadian Black Watch named Robert E. Sherwood, its photography editor. Mrs. Parker's reviews were notoriously caustic, but when she wrote that Billie Burke "plays her lighter scenes rather as if she were giving an impression of Eva Tanguay," Miss Burke's husband Florenz Ziegfeld notified *Vanity Fair* that the magazine could choose between his advertising and Mrs. Parker's services. On the day she was fired, Sherwood and Benchley resigned in protest. Benchley's job had lasted almost nine months. "I was getting in a rut," he shrugged.

Now he found himself once more facing the problem of eking out a living. He and Mrs. Parker rented a joint office in the shabby old Metropolitan Opera House building, a secret retreat so tiny that Benchley remarked, "If it were any smaller, it would have constituted adultery." Legend has it that they printed a sign on the door: UTICA DROP FORGE & TOOL COMPANY, ROBERT BENCHLEY, PRESIDENT. DOROTHY PARKER, PRESIDENT and worked out the cable address of "Park-bench." Legend adds that day after day they sat at their respective typewriters in unbroken seclusion until Mrs. Parker, restless for company, suggested that the door sign should be changed to read: MEN.

Robert Sherwood had been hired as movie critic of *Life,* and Benchley, whose previous contributions had been summarily rejected by that magazine, was suddenly invited to become its drama reviewer. It was a job for which he was admirably suited. He loved the theater, and his criticisms were good-natured and gentle. If the play amused him, his infectious belly laugh could be heard throughout the theater—Brooks Atkinson remembers that "Benchley exploded like a dynamite pit"—and the delighted cast did not have to wait for his printed judgment. If he were bored, an instinctive courtesy kept him from betraying his feelings.

Only once did Benchley's good nature desert him. In May of 1922 a play by Anne Nichols, called *Abie's Irish Rose,* opened at the Fulton, the evening after a dismal flop called *The Rotters,* which Benchley described in *Life* as "the worst play of the season." Upon seeing Miss Nichols's effort, he added: "On the night following the presentation of 'The Rotters,' residents of Broadway, New York City, were startled by the sound of horses' hoofs clattering up the famous thoroughfare. Rushing to their windows, they saw a man, in Colonial costume, riding a bay mare from whose eyes flashed fire. The man was shouting as he rode, and his message was: ' "The Rotters" is no longer the worst play in town: "Abie's Irish Rose" has just opened!' "

Unfortunately Benchley had established the custom of following his weekly criticism with brief summaries of previous reviews, called "Confidential Guide," which he rewrote for each successive issue; and as *Abie's Irish Rose* continued to flourish month after month, despite its negative notices, Benchley found himself hard put to invent new ways of saying "Among the season's worst" or "Something awful." His frantic struggles to improvise became a public joke: People bought *Life* just to read such efforts at evasion as "There is no letter *W* in the French alphabet" or "Flying fish are sometimes seen at as great a height as fifteen feet" or "Will the Marines *never* come?" When the cast of *Abie* sent him a derisive birthday cake on the first anniversary of its spectacular run, he noted feebly: "To be reviewed next week." The play set a Broadway record of 2,327 performances, and by the fifth year Benchley was reduced to holding a prize contest for suggestions. Harpo Marx won with "No worse than a bad cold."

Frank Sullivan voiced the feelings of Benchley's innumerable friends after his untimely death in 1945: "Just to meet him and say Hello was a tonic. For my own selfish part, I give thanks that he lived in this age, for that happy circumstance enabled me to have the rich, joyous, and rewarding experience of knowing him, and delighting in him."

NINA WARNER HOOKE

A Glimpse of Eden

THE SEAL WAS FIRST SEEN by a fisherman named Alan Lander one evening early in May. Alan and his father were dropping their crab pots about half a mile out from the cove when the animal bobbed up near their boat. It sat on its tail, with the upper half of its body out of the water, and watched the men at their work. When they tossed the onlooker one of the whiting they had brought for crab bait, the seal instantly dived, apparently frightened by the sight of fish flung through the air. On the next tide, when the men went to haul their pots, they saw the seal again, but the next morning it had gone. Two days later, however, it was back, stretched out on a ledge beside the cove.

The cove is a wild place, not far from my village on England's Dorset coast. It is called Chapman's Pool. To reach it, you must leave your car on the headland and make your way 400 feet down over slippery blue clay that constantly crumbles and shifts. The pool lies in a half-circle of shale cliffs, which recede into uncultivated hills grazed by roaming cattle. Hares and foxes live in the thickets. Man has left little mark. The beach, of pebbles and coarse sand, is strewn with fallen boulders, flotsam, and sometimes the carcass of a heifer that reached too far for the sea cabbage growing on the cliff.

In wintry weather, when sea and sky are gray as the shale, the scene is somber. But on a still, bright day in summer the pool is a jewel in a pewter setting. It is a timeless place, the quietest I know. Nothing moves but a leaping fish or a plunging cormorant. There is no sound but the slap of waves.

"I thought the seal was ill," Alan Lander says. "But it was just sunning itself there on the shore."

All that day it stayed close to the water, eyeing the men warily, and at dusk it vanished. When I came down to the cove to see the seal at the end of the week, it had put in three more appearances, and the men had grown accustomed to its presence. It seemed to like the sound of their voices. They had tried to lure it closer with freshly caught pollack, but the animal was impervious to bribes.

On the afternoon I arrived, tatters of mist were hanging on the hills and creeping over the water. There was no sign of the seal.

"It came in this morning and then went off again," Alan shouted. "I doubt if it's far away. Try hollering."

"You mean, *call* it?"

"That's right."

Very self-conscious, I cupped my hands and called, *"Hullo-oo!"* Some startled gulls rose from the rocks. Nothing else happened.

"Hullo-oo-oo!" I called again. And suddenly, far out in the pool, a gleaming thing surfaced, a wedge-shaped, eerily human form standing in a ribbon of mist. It seemed to hang there for a long moment, then it began to swim toward us. It stopped within three yards of the shore, half in and half out of the water, head raised and eyes calm and bright.

I had never been so close to a seal outside a zoo. The animal had molting fur, faded and patchy—quite different from the frosty gray sheen and velvety texture of its new coat. Our visitor, subsequently identified as a male Atlantic gray seal about eighteen months old, was a little over four-and-a-half-feet long. When he opened his jaws, we saw a formidable set of pointed teeth. He had white whiskers that looked like plastic. The wide-open eyes were quite round, and they mirrored every mood.

While I seemed to perceive some sense of recognition within both the seal and me, I didn't feel that I could safely touch him. By the second week he had become so fearless that he would flop down beside me when I sat on the beach. He seemed to be inviting me to pet him, but still I did not dare. Those jaws could snap a hand off.

One day when I was not on the beach, a couple spending a holiday in a nearby cottage brought their four-year-old daughter to see the "tame" seal at the cove. Racing ahead, she reached the beach where the seal lay sunning itself while her parents were still at the top of the ravine. They shouted, but she ran straight to the seal and began hugging and kissing it.

When her parents caught up, she was crooning, "Dear doggie, good doggie," and the seal was responding with obvious delight. His flippers clasped the child, and he was making a strange moaning sound. The two played all afternoon, and when the family left, there were tears.

After that we did not hesitate to pet him. He liked to have his stomach rubbed and the top of his head stroked. He would return our caresses by hugging us, or by mouthing our arms or legs between his teeth. Once he took my throat in his jaws, but so gently the skin was unmarked.

By late May the seal had taken complete possession of the pool. His amiability on shore had been proved, but the water was his own element. How would he react when swimming started at the cove? To find out, I put on a swimsuit one afternoon and walked to the water's edge. The seal followed, flopped into the water, and looked at me inquiringly. I returned his gaze, trying to project my intention, and then I stepped off to stand beside him in the waist-deep water.

He had evidently thought us exclusively land animals until that moment. His look of surprise changed to one of joy. He swam close, put his flippers around my waist and pushed his muzzle into my neck, moaning in his characteristic way. Pushing him gently away, I began to show that I was able to romp with him in the sea as I did on land. He seemed to grasp this, and his excitement was apparent. He dived, surfaced, rolled like a porpoise, pulled me along by an arm or a leg, and drew me underwater till our faces met.

Anyone who has played with an aquatic animal in its own element can never forget the beauty of the experience. The seal's clumsiness on land is the penalty it pays for perfection in the water, where it is all grace and power. However, this power made the seal capable of dragging me down in deep water where he was at home and I was not. It seemed prudent to accustom him to these games in the shallows before venturing deeper.

Before long, holiday visitors would be coming to the pool. We not only had to be sure the seal represented no danger to swimmers, but we had to insure his own safety as well. While we considered that he might be safer if no one knew about him, we finally decided that if he became a well-known attraction on the holiday coast, no one would dare harm him. We gave accounts to local newspapers, and the publicity brought many sightseers to the cove as summer weather came on.

The seal welcomed petting from crowds of strangers. He became something of a pest as he grew used to people—knocking over small children, flopping down soaking wet in the middle of picnics, blowing fishy breath over the sandwiches, snapping at dogs, and frightening old ladies. But he had no interest in anything edible except freshly caught fish, and even these he seemed to accept more to please the giver than himself. By mid-June he had calmed down, causing trouble only when small dogs yapped at him.

He reserved his love—as opposed to liking, which he gave indiscriminately—for the few people who would swim with him in deep water. There were never more than two or three at any time during the summer, and perhaps because I was the first, I seemed to be his favorite. Until the end of June, however, we all resisted his efforts to draw us out of the shallows.

One morning when I went to the cove, I called to him from the top of the ravine. Instantly he headed inshore and was waiting for me when I reached the beach. The cove was empty except for us. It was a wonderful morning, the pool like a sheet of glass under a sunny sky. He laid his head in my lap, and I stroked him till he nodded off. I had a sudden impulse to try swimming with him in deep water while he was in this languid mood.

He was asleep when I waded in, and I had swum 50 yards before he waked up and followed me. He dived under me and bobbed up in front, his eyes round with surprise. He looked like an anxious nanny saying, "Ought you to come so far?"

In the middle of the pool, where the depth is about twenty feet, I rested. He joined me, turned on his back, too, and we floated side by side. As the tide rocked us closer together, I reached for his flipper and held it. He turned his head to gaze into my face. I felt that I was looking back through time to the world before man was shunned by all other living things. It was like a glimpse of Eden.

This was the first of the unforgettable days. June went out in a heat wave, and I went to the cove as often as I could. His sight was so keen that he could recognize me far up the ravine. He barked and whined with impatience to get into the water, then plunged in ahead of me and waited. We would swim to the mouth of the cove and beyond, around the eastern reef to the lonely bay under St. Aldhelm's Head. I would rest on a boulder while the seal cruised about. Sometimes he caught a small fish, ate it under water, then sat up and wiped his face with his flippers. It was a joyous succession of days.

I saw less of him in August, when I spent many rainy and windy days at home working to finish the play I was writing. But I heard accounts of the "tame" seal, and I was assured that he was safe and well. August wore on, and then September, and I found it increasingly hard to find time to visit the beach.

In October I was too busy to get down to the pool more than two or three times. His other devotees reported that the seal welcomed them with extravagant delight. As they left, he followed them to the foot of the ravine, whining and crying.

One October night I ran into Alan Lander. "It's my belief he'll be gone afore long," Alan said. "It's the loneliness. He can't stand it."

"But it doesn't make sense. His natural life is a lonely one."

"Say what you like, but it's my belief he'll make off."

I went home feeling disturbed, and that night I had a dream about the seal. Our customary roles were reversed, and it was he who called, and I who came. Fully clothed, I waded in and swam to him, but he drew farther out to the sea each time I approached, until I was alone in a waste of water far from shore.

Next day the weather turned to gales and thunderstorms that raged for a week. My thoughts were constantly on the cove, and at last I telephoned my friend Percy at the coast-guard station.

"Is he there still?"

"Yes. But if you want to see him again, you'd better go quick. We heard him howling last night, under the Head. I reckon he'll make off tomorrow."

It puzzled me that both men seemed so sure, but I knew better than to scoff at men who live close to the sea. I immediately drove down to the cove. From above, the bay looked deserted, but finally I saw him lying on the beach. The tide was high, and a big sea was running. I had to pick my way close under the cliff to reach him. He welcomed me with a great display of affection, but his eyes looked troubled. He kept shaking his head and whining. I sensed he was trying to tell me something I already knew. I sat down and took his head on my lap, stroking it and talking softly to him.

After a while my legs became cramped and I got up. He moved away from me down toward the water, looking searchingly at me. Suddenly I was reminded so vividly of my dream that I stumbled back in panic, then stared down at him with my heart pounding. While I hesitated, torn between fear and a longing to go to him, a wave ran halfway up the beach and licked at my feet. I turned and ran, scrambling from rock to rock between the crashing seas till I reached the ravine. The clay, soft with rain, clung to my shoes and held me back. In a kind of desperation I clawed my way to the top.

When I looked down, muddied and gasping for breath, I saw that the seal had swum out to watch me climb. Now he was far out in the pool, still watching, a dark dot in the fading light.

I never saw him again.

JACOB HAY

The Reformation
of Fogarty

IF THE AMERICAN ART WORLD HAD KNOWN that Alexandre Dumas
Fogarty was bored during that April of 1956, and if it had had the
slightest inkling of what the awesome consequences of this ennui
would be, the American art world would have trembled in its
boots.

A vast man, Alexandre Dumas Fogarty, but tall enough to carry
his avoirdupois with grace and agility—which was frequently necessary in the cramped confines of the flying bridge of the *Brave
Musketeer* (ex-Royal Navy Motor Gunboat No. 745) which, in
turn, was the principal asset of the Trans-Mediterranean Custom
Freight Express Service, with headquarters in the then international city of Tangier.

This enterprise had discontinued operations when its owner,
A. D. Fogarty, had observed the increasingly effective cooperation
between the French and Italian customs services, and noted that
both of those splendid organizations were equipping themselves
with newer and more powerful launches against whose engines
the elderly Rolls-Royces of the *Brave Musketeer* were proving less
and less capable of competition. Then, too, by 1956, the European
market for American nylons, cigarettes, and bonded bourbon was
being adequately supplied through more normal channels of im-
port.

48

So Fogarty had retired to Rome to enjoy the beauties of that fabled city and to give thought to his future. The mere thought of returning to his family's dental supply business in Perth Amboy, N. J., caused him to shudder; for while there is much to be said for the false tooth industry, it cannot be denied that it lacks much of romance and excitement, two qualities without which Fogarty found life unendurable.

But for a robust, vital man, accustomed to a life of instant decisions and strenuous activity, even the splendors of Rome, bathed in that city's magical light, can begin to pall. Thus it was with Alexandre Dumas Fogarty, as he sat at his table that April afternoon on the sidewalk before Danielo's on the Via Veneto, his ruddy face a study in boredom beneath the blue beret which concealed his crew-cut red hair. His glass of Lacrimae Christi stood untouched on the table's marble surface; his cigarette smoldered unnoted in the ashtray, which extolled the merits of a renowned stomach bitters.

Then, suddenly, a curious light shone in his steel-gray eyes and a slow smile spread across the rugged expanses of his cheeks. The hour was precisely 10:30 a.m., Rome Time.

Thousands of miles to the west, in the curator's office of the Wilma L. Blastfogle Memorial Art Museum, brightest jewel in the cultural crown of that admirable third-class city, Dexter, Pa., Miss Clarissa Saunders shivered involuntarily.

"Anything wrong, Miss Saunders?" asked her assistant, Miss Eustacia Wilkes, her tone concerned for her superior.

"Nothing, really," Miss Saunders replied quickly, with a light laugh. "Somebody walking over my grave, as my grandmother used to put it."

"Oh," said Miss Wilkes, enlightened. She glanced at the wall clock. "Four thirty—almost time to be thinking about closing up." And the incident was forgotten.

Alexandre Dumas Fogarty had remembered the di Venati brothers of Naples. More important, his future lay clear before him, sparkling with promise. And with gold.

Shortly before the Trans-Mediterranean Custom Freight Express Service ceased to exist, Fogarty had attended to a problem on behalf of an eminent, albeit unscrupulous, Italian capitalist who desired to transfer a not inconsiderable amount of gold to his bank in Tangier without submitting to the bothersome formalities normally required by the Italian government in transactions of this nature. A Neapolitan acquaintance had, sometime previously, introduced Fogarty to the brothers, Giovanni and Ernesto, who were manufacturers, in a small way, of religious statues and other objects of piety. Fogarty recalled their conversation.

"It is true that sales have slowed," Giovanni had conceded after he had listened to Fogarty's proposition over a bottle of Orvieto in the brothers' favorite café. "What with the communists and their anticlerical views, people just aren't buying the way they used to in the old days. We can no longer afford to be as selective about what commissions we undertake."

"What he is trying to say, Signore," Ernesto had put in, a trifle impatiently, "is that we'll take the job."

In consequence of these negotiations the gold was transformed into several dozen small Saint Christophers, and these, painted in glowing colors, were passed through the Italian customs with the ease customarily associated with the theft of candy from a baby.

When they were not engaged in the creation and casting of their religious artifacts, the di Venatis devoted themselves to the cleaning and restoration of older works of church art, and the excellent state of preservation of the medieval and Renaissance statuary and painting so notable in many of the Neapolitan churches may be attributed in large measure to their loving craftsmanship and devotion.

Fogarty took the afternoon express to Naples.

"But what you suggest would be, in effect, forgery, Signore," Ernesto di Venati protested over another bottle of Orvieto.

"Not forgery, my dear Ernesto, but *reproduction*—simple, honest *reproduction*," Fogarty explained patiently as he signaled the waiter to bring a replacement for the first bottle. His eyes beamed with sheer integrity. "Why, my dear chap, the market for *reproductions* of fine art in the United States surpasses the imagination. Even the humblest housewife longs for the day when she can hang a Rembrandt over her television set, and no merchant of any substance would be caught dead without one or two bits of Greek statuary about his residence."

"Incredible," muttered Ernesto. "And one has always dismissed the Americans as gross materialists."

"We would have to take on another painter," Giovanni mused. "There is that young Pasquale Torsini, who lives just around the corner and is courting my Gina."

"A brilliant boy," Ernesto agreed with enthusiasm. "And he will not demand the moon as salary."

"You understand," Fogarty cautioned the brothers, "that I can undertake to market these reproductions only on condition that they represent the pinnacle of your artistic powers, only if they are absolutely indistinguishable from the originals in style, materials, and rendering. The American housewife, gentlemen, is a keen and observant customer, and nothing but the best will part her from her housekeeping dollar."

"But of a certainty," Ernesto and Giovanni replied as one man. "If it comes from the workshops of the di Venati," Ernesto added, "it will come only when it is perfection, or not at all. Thus it has been in our family for the past three centuries, and thus it will remain. You have our word on it, Signor Fogarty. And now it is our turn to buy . . . if you have never sampled the Apulian Sansevero, you have never truly tasted our finest white wines."

In this fashion, with nothing more than a manly handclasp to bind their bargain and the ancient honor of the di Venatis and the Fogartys to uphold it, was established a partnership which was to create history of a sort—and chaos—in the American art world.

While the brothers set about their end of the business, Fogarty occupied himself with the more delicate matter of securing the services of one Antonio Fragelli, of whose special skill, developed during years in the Italian underground, he now had need. Fragelli had long since graduated from such comparatively simple challenges as German identity papers and frontier passes. Additionally, he had enlarged his eerie talents by massive doses of scholarly research.

Given half a day, Fragelli could compose a screed attesting the authenticity of a medieval reliquary, written in the somewhat debauched Latin of the period and signed by a bishop, the whole on ancient parchment, and backed in depth by a latter-day typewritten statement on the engraved letterhead of the Italian Government bureau charged with the preservation of national art treasures. His rendering of the signature of the late and renowned art critic, Bernard Berenson, it was generally agreed, partook of the nature of a masterpiece.

Fragelli's eyes gleamed when Fogarty outlined his needs.

"Magnificent," he cried, overcome by emotion at the conclusion of Fogarty's remarks. "For years I have awaited a project with the scope to match my art. I am in your debt, Signor Fogarty, and you may cease to worry about the problem of documentation."

Fragelli was also commissioned to prepare a British passport and necessary supporting papers for a Dr. Andrew Duff Frazer, formerly Associate Consultant to the British War Office in the matter of restoring works of art to the various galleries and museums from which they had been looted by the Nazis during World War II. This was, Fogarty felt, an identity at once respectable and vague enough to defy all but the most persistent tracing. Too, the name would offer protection against the accidental display of one of his monogrammed handkerchiefs.

Of his association with Fragelli, Fogarty said nothing to the di Venatis. The honest brothers might not have understood. In the meantime, Fogarty devoted himself to a deep study of scholarly works on the history of art, and spent what little leisure he permitted himself in listening to the overseas broadcasts of the British Broadcasting Corporation in order to perfect Dr. Andrew Duff Frazer's Oxonian accent.

In shortly less than six months the di Venatis and young Pasquale Torsini produced enough art treasures to stock a small gallery, each one—although they were unaware of this interesting fact—supplied with a completely fraudulent history fully and carefully documented by the masterful forgeries of Signor Fragelli. Among other items there were a hitherto unknown Tiepolo, found after centuries of neglect in the attic of a Venetian palace; several Canalettos, discovered among the effects of an Italian nobleman who had died in poverty, unaware of the wealth on his walls; and representative works of the Dutch and Flemish schools. In addition, there were half a dozen Etruscan bronzes and an equal number of exquisite late Greek marbles. These last the imaginative Ernesto—without prompting from Fogarty—had carefully shattered and then reconstructed, artfully leaving several chips out here and there.

"It gives them a nice antique finish," he had explained to a charmed and secretly delighted Fogarty.

"I think I'm ready for Rembrandt," young Pasquale Torsini declared the day Fogarty set sail for America with his counterfeit trove.

"Don't rush yourself, lad," Fogarty told him kindly. "But if you feel you're up to it, by all means!" He turned to the Brothers di Venati. "If this first shipment sells well, gentlemen, I feel we can turn next to some Cretan potteries, a few pieces of Egyptian funerary sculpture, and perhaps a few Byzantine icons."

"Possibly a small Michaelangelo, say, and a Cellini saltcellar?" Giovanni asked wistfully. "Nothing too elaborate, mind you."

"I leave it to your judgment with full confidence," Fogarty declared stoutly, taking their hands for a farewell clasp.

"A small going-away present," murmured Fragelli, who had come down to the pier for the sailing. Fogarty had introduced him simply as an old acquaintance, not wishing to disturb the high moral sense of the di Venatis and young Torsini. Now the master forger pressed a large envelope into Fogarty's hand.

"It is a letter of introduction for you from the Duke of Edinburgh," he said shyly. Fogarty was much moved by his kindness, since Fragelli had already written, at his regular rates, similar letters from the director of the Tate Gallery and the curator of fine arts at the Louvre, both of whom had nothing but the highest regard for the professional integrity of Dr. Andrew Duff Frazer.

Thus armed, Alexandre Dumas Fogarty descended on the United States.

With that wisdom bred from his experience in developing the Trans-Mediterranean Custom Freight Express Service, Fogarty elected not to test his skill in the big leagues until he had had an opportunity to polish it in the minors. In consequence, he concentrated his efforts on the newer and smaller museums and galleries which the American national prosperity has seen fostered in almost every city with any pretensions to civic pride. He warmed up, as it were, on the municipal museums and privately endowed galleries of such far-flung centers of culture as Evansville, Indiana, and Charlotte, North Carolina, and Akron, Ohio. Only after his merchandise and documents had successfully withstood the scrutiny of the officials of these lesser institutions did he move into the more hazardous dealings involved with the older and larger establishments.

Discretion forbids, even now, the public humiliation which would result from a revelation of the full list of Fogarty's major victims. Suffice it to say that the unknown Tiepolo hangs to this day in one of the largest museums in the east. Admittedly, the plaque identifying it bears a question mark after the artist's name, but even so, its presence says much for the skill and versatility of Pasquale Torsini.

Unloading the bogus horde took roughly six months, at the end of which period some twenty museums had paid Fogarty approximately $250,000 for his wares. It was, he decided, time to withdraw from the field—while he was ahead. There was always the possibility that he might encounter some museum director with the elementary common sense to write to the British War Office concerning the antecedents of Dr. Andrew Duff Frazer. Then, too, the letter from the Duke of Edinburgh—as gracious a note as a man might wish to receive from royalty—was becoming a trifle frayed at the folds.

In line with this decision he wrote to the di Venati brothers, explaining to them that, successful as sales had been, he was reluctantly obliged to retire from business on the advice of his physician—an old war wound was giving him a bit of trouble. With the letter he enclosed a check for $25,000 as their share of the receipts and by way of recompense for further work they may have put into preparation.

The brothers di Venati wrote back most gratefully, expressing regret and the hope that his health would soon enable him to resume their mutually profitable relationship.

All in all, Fogarty felt, it had been an entirely amicable and satisfactory transaction—although he later reproached himself bitterly for not sending for the Cellini saltcellar.

Thereafter Dr. Andrew Duff Frazer vanished from the face of the earth, and for the next several years Fogarty lived the life of a gentleman of leisure in the small but exquisitely appointed villa he had purchased in Villefranche on the French Riviera. He dabbled in water colors and girl-watching, and resisted several determined assaults on his bachelorhood.

Now it might be thought that Fogarty should have been content to rest on his laurels; but the truth is that in so doing, Fogarty would have failed to achieve the ultimate exploitation of his grand plan. Unlike the Roman period, these years were not ones of boredom; he was simply waiting for his plan to mature, and while he waited he devoted much of his time to polishing the details.

At the end of four patient years he began growing a beard of massive proportions. At the end of the fifth year he returned to the United States—as Alexandre Dumas Fogarty.

A. D. Fogarty, the art sleuth.

A brief and secretive reunion with the admirable Fragelli had produced yet another set of documents, signed by the highest authorities, validating his status. It was for this occasion that Fragelli created a warm and charming note of introduction from Mr.

Berenson, acknowledging A. D. Fogarty as his peer in the field of artistic criticism.

"Alexandre was always a secretive, moody lad," declared T. J. Fogarty, president of the Atlantic Dental Supply Corporation and Fogarty's only surviving relative, on later questioning by the press. "We had no idea what he was up to all those years in Europe."

For the truth is, Alexandre Dumas Fogarty hit the American art world like a copper-bearded thunderbolt. He had, he advised the art editor of The New York *Intelligencer,* been conducting certain studies in art forgeries when word had reached him of a vast scheme perpetrated some years previously by a renegade Englishman on a number of American museums. Outraged, he had traced this report, sparing himself no effort, and had at last located in Naples the three Italian artists who had been the innocent dupes of this sinister Briton. They had freely admitted their manufacture of art reproductions which they sincerely believed would be sold as such, and were appalled when informed that this had not been the case. No, they did not know to which museums their innocent forgeries had been sold, but they would and could furnish complete descriptions of all their bogus antiquities.

From coast to coast museum curators began living in a nightmare as Fogarty moved among them—naturally charging a handsome fee for his services. The director of the Walla Walla, Wash., Municipal Center for the Fine Arts resigned under a cloud when Fogarty pointed out no less than three fake Holbeins from the brush of Pasquale Torsini, to cite only one instance. And then Fogarty encountered a mystery of increasingly disturbing proportions. Some of his fakes had vanished.

When you are charging a museum several thousand bucks for your professional services as a detector of forgeries, it comes as a rude shock to discover that the forgery you have so carefully planted is no longer around to be detected. Thus the Etruscan bronze that Fogarty had foisted off on Charlotte, North Carolina, was no longer edifying the culture-hungry of that Piedmontese city; the Canaletto he had unloaded on Evansville, Indiana, was no longer the pride of that Ohio River municipality.

It took him a long and desperately boring evening with one Dr. Theobald Terwilliger, curator of the Harrison T. Waller Memorial Gallery, of Harrisburg, Pa., to ascertain what had happened. He had dined Dr. Terwilliger in the finest restaurant in Harrisburg, plying him with preprandial cocktails, wines of the richest and most delicate vintages (as these things are understood in Harrisburg), and postprandial brandy dating from the fall of the House of Hohenzollern.

"But I was certain that I had read something in the magazines about your museum's purchase of a hitherto unknown Van Baburen," Fogarty told Terwilliger in the injured tones of a man whose memory has betrayed him. A cunning gleam lighted Terwilliger's eyes, and Fogarty swiftly ordered him another brandy.

"Fact ish,-er, is," Terwilliger said in a conspiratorial whisper, "we did." He giggled nervously. "Got had three ways from Shunday on that one. Trushteesh would have thrown a fit, if they'd ever dish,-er, discovered it."

"But *you* did?" Fogarty asked incredulously.

"Shpotted that Englishman—just about your shize, come to think of it—like I shay, shpotted him for a phoney the minute I laid eyesh of him." (My foot, Fogarty thought angrily.)

"And so?" Fogarty could not conceal his eagerness.

"Well, you know how it goes in this bish—business, confound it! What I mean to shay ish, ask me no queshions and I'll tell you no liesh. Maybe this Englishman had got hold of the real thing, and how wasn't any of my affair. I mean, it *looked* like the real thing to me. Sho I bought it." (And how well I remember *that* transaction, Fogarty thought. Terwilliger cleverly haggling over the price, and his undisguised triumph when I permitted him to knock me down to his final offer. Nasty little man!)

"And then?"

"Got to thinking. Shent a sample of the canvash down to the

National Gallery in Washington. They shent it back with a note telling me it had been made in England between 1926 and 1931. Ol' Van Baburen died in 1624. Shimple?" Terwilliger accepted still another brandy. "Sort of thing could cost a man his job in this racket, fy'undershtand? Sho, I did the only shensible thing I could do under the shircumshtanches—I unloaded it."

"Where?" Fogarty asked, masking his shock at this creature's base duplicity.

"Dexter, tha'sh where. Go shee Clarissha Shaunders, down in Dexter. Shweet girl, really shweet, but naive, you follow me?"

"If you won't tell, neither will I," Fogarty advised this vessel of deceit.

"You're all heart, Fogarty," Terwilliger replied, choking up.

"Forget it," Alexandre Dumas said, his tone edged with contempt. "Some day I may be able to put you in line for a Cellini saltcellar."

As a result of this conversation, Fogarty journeyed to Dexter, a spotlessly clean little city in the heart of the Pennsylvania Dutch country, full of rosy-cheeked natives who spoke a dialect somewhere between Prussian and Middle English. Registering at the Hotel Phineas Dexter, the community's principal hostelry, he made his way to the Wilma L. Blastfogle Memorial Art Museum, which occupied a vast old townhouse near the city's center. Unobtrusively and as a typically interested visitor, he wandered through its various rooms.

What he found staggered him.

Theobald Terwilliger had not been the only one of his esoteric calling to unload on the naive Miss Clarissa Saunders. This innocent female had been bilked by no less than a dozen of her professional colleagues—for there before Fogarty's bewildered eyes were gathered all those of his forgeries missing elsewhere. All, all were there—including Akron's Grecian boxer and the superb Van Dyck that once graced the Confederate Memorial Gallery of the Living Arts of Augusta, Ga.

Fogarty stood bemused; he was by no means a cruel man, and the prospect of what his disclosures would do to the career of Miss Clarissa Saunders gave him pause.

On the other hand this foolish woman had done him out of thousands of dollars he might otherwise have received for his detective services. By her passion to acquire additional treasures to sweeten the memory of the late Wilma L. Blastfogle, she had deprived him of the rightful fruits of his toil.

Fogarty steeled his heart and made for the curator's office.

"Miss Saunders is out at the moment," Miss Eustacia Wilkes informed him. "Can I help you?"

"I am Alexandre Dumas Fogarty. Perhaps you have heard of me?"

"Yes, indeed, sir. The famous art detective. Miss Saunders will be so thrilled." Miss Wilkes stared with undisguised admiration at Fogarty's magnificent copper-colored beard.

"Then if you would be good enough to ask her to call me at my hotel." And with a courteous bow, Fogarty withdrew.

He had not been in his room more than half an hour when the telephone rang and he heard for the first time the dulcet tones of Clarissa Saunders. It would be well, he decided, to have a look at this female before he set about the fearsome task of destroying her, and he therefore suggested that she meet him in the Baron von Steuben Room, the hotel's mock-Revolutionary cocktail lounge.

"I'd love to," she rejoined cheerfully. "Give me fifteen minutes. I'll recognize you by your beard."

Fogarty hung up, feeling a distinct sense of unease. He had expected the dry, crisp tones of an elderly and opinionated spinster, not the gay and girlish sounds he had heard.

Nevertheless, he had his duty to perform.

His waiter had just set his Martini before him when the heavy wood-slab door of the Baron von Steuben Room opened to disclose a tall, slender, and absolutely the most ravishing woman Fogarty had beheld in all thirty-six years of his bachelorhood. She was clad in a misty pink sweater and gray flannel skirt that outlined modestly and without undue emphasis a figure of truly classic proportions.

This vision of blonde loveliness swiftly adjusted her vision to the dimness of the room, and catching sight of the only beard then present, she walked surely and gracefully towards Fogarty's table, her hand outstretched and a smile on her perfectly shaped lips.

Fogarty staggered to his feet, confounded.

"You must be Mr. Fogarty," she said as they shook hands. "I've been reading so much about you lately. Welcome to Dexter."

She slipped into the chair opposite his with the lithe movement of a ballet dancer, and he felt his senses reeling even as he inhaled the first faint fragrance of her perfume. "Same as yours," she added when he asked for her preference in refreshment. Another Martini was forthwith furnished.

"I take it," she said calmly, "you've been through the museum."

Fogarty nodded unhappily. "Merely a cursory inspection," he muttered, unable to take his eyes from her face, a face which would have fetched a shout of joy from Renoir, a moan of ecstasy from Monet. "Just passing through and thought I'd drop by for a look around."

"Fine," said this splendid young woman equably. "What do you think of my fakes?"

Alexandre Dumas stared at her, dumfounded.

"Fakes?" he finally managed to croak.

"One of the finest collections in the east," she declared, grinning proudly.

"But . . . if you knew they were fakes, why . . . ?" Fogarty stopped, for once in his life at a loss for words. Clarissa's face (unaccountably, he found himself already thinking of her as Clarissa) grew abruptly grave.

"Because I've got a tiny budget, and because they're good fakes —so good they fooled some of my pompous friends in the big museums," she said quietly, "Dexter might never have seen a Canaletto if it weren't for my forgery, and does it really matter that much if my Van Dyck isn't a true Van Dyck? The point is, it's the best imitation of Van Dyck this town can afford; it has his style and composition, even down to his brushwork. That's what counts. Now Dexter knows what a Van Dyck looks like and can really appreciate him."

"But your trustees?" Fogarty gurgled—he was aghast at her frankness.

"They've known from the beginning, ever since that insufferable little man, Terwilliger, from Harrisburg, offered me his fake Van Baburen. After all, I'm in touch with the National Gallery, too. But I put it to the trustees that Dexter might never see Van Baburen's work and style otherwise. And I will say for the Pennsylvania Dutch that they're realists. My trustees are behind me to a man, bless their hearts."

"And the townspeople? The local newspapers? Do they know?" Visions of a tar-and-feather party filled Fogarty's brain.

"Certainly they know. What's more important, they understand and approve of what I'm trying to do. We've got a fine representative collection of art which, if it were all genuine, we simply could never hope to have. You know, Mr. Fogarty, I'd like to meet the character who brought all this stuff in from Europe; for my money, he deserves a medal."

"Miss Saunders," Fogarty began unsteadily, his emotions clouding his vision and lumping his throat.

"Call me Clarissa," she said, dimpling beautifully, "and I don't mind if I do have another Martini, Mr. Fogarty."

"Call me Alex," Fogarty begged in tones that rang with sincerity. "And Clarissa, there's something I feel I ought to tell you . . ."

The Fogartys are living in Paris now, Alexandre Dumas having sold the villa in Villefranche and Mrs. Fogarty having resigned her post with the Wilma L. Blastfogle Memorial Art Museum to accompany her husband in his new career as a buyer of art (legitimate) for sale in the American market. True, they deal extensively in reproductions, each carefully labeled as a product of the di Venati Brothers shops, Naples, Italy; and their reputation among American art dealers is second to none.

Only one reminder of Fogarty's former ways is to be seen in their charming flat off the Boulevard Haussmann. Mrs. Fogarty refuses flatly to part with it. It is a saltcellar, widely attributed to Cellini.

"Alexandre Dumas Cellini, that is," Fogarty tells awed dinner guests, grinning above his spectacular red beard.

The beard? Why of course he still has it. There's no explaining a woman's reasoning, but Clarissa simply won't let him shave it off. She likes it.

TOM MAHONEY

The First Airman
Across America

PILOTS FLY JET PLANES so fast, frequently, and uneventfully between New York and California today that it is hard to realize that less than 60 years ago no pilot had flown any kind of plane across America. The man who showed the way was Calbraith Perry Rodgers, a stubborn, courageous 6-foot 4-inch, 192-pounder, who actually smoked a cigar while flying the early, open, wingwarping Wright planes.

He was the descendant of so many brave men that he simply had to win glory of some kind. His father, an Army captain, had been killed fighting Indians in Arizona. One of his great-grandfathers, Commodore Matthew Calbraith Perry, opened Japan to the world. A grand-uncle, Commodore Oliver Hazard Perry, won the Battle of Lake Erie and sent the famous message: "We have met the enemy and they are ours . . ." An earlier ancestor, Commodore John Rodgers, dictated peace terms to the Algerian pirates.

An attack of scarlet fever when he was a six-year-old boy in Havre de Grace, Md., dashed "Cal" Rodgers' hopes of a military career. The fever left him so deaf that he could not pass the physical examination when appointed to the U.S. Naval Academy. At

63

about the same time his slightly younger double cousin, John Rodgers, passed the examination. Their fathers had married sisters. While John went on to Annapolis and a Navy career, Cal played football at Virginia and Columbia, then became a motorcycle and automobile race driver.

But when Lt. John Rodgers was sent to the Wright Brothers' flying school in the summer of 1911 and became the second Navy flyer (after Theodore G. Ellyson and ahead of John H. Towers), Cal Rodgers decided to become a flyer too. He went to the Wright Brothers' school at his own expense, learned to fly with only 90 minutes' instruction, and paid $5,000 for a frail Wright biplane.

He established an endurance flight record of 3 hours and 42 minutes, and spent 27 of the 33 flying hours of the meet in the air. He won $11,000 in prizes with his biplane at an air competition in Chicago's Grant Park, August 12-20, 1911. There he met J. Ogden Armour, who was attempting to diversify his meat packing business by launching a grape soda pop named Vin Fiz. As a publicity stunt for this drink, he backed Rodgers in an effort to win the biggest aviation prize then unclaimed. Unlike some other early flyers, Rodgers did not touch hard liquor and the tie-up was a logical one.

The prize was $50,000, offered by William Randolph Hearst, the newspaper publisher, for the first flight across the U.S. The country had neither airways nor airports and the farthest anybody had flown had been 1,155 miles. This had been Harry Atwood's 11-day St. Louis-to-N.Y. flight with many stops. Hearst said nothing about stops, but the trip had to be made in 30 days and be completed by Oct. 11, 1911, a year from the day he posted the prize. Rodgers thought he could win by flying 200 miles a day.

He named his plane *The Vin Fiz Flyer,* and painted the name on several parts of the machine. He agreed to drop leaflets from the air advertising the 5¢ purple product. In return, Armour contracted to pay him $5 for every mile flown and outfitted a special railroad train to accompany him. This consisted of a Pullman, a combination diner-observation car, and a "hangar" baggage car.

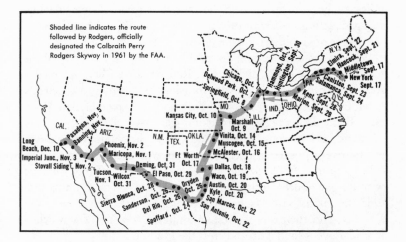

The last carried a type "B" airplane, two engines, a six-cylinder Palmer-Singer touring car, a machine shop, and a first-aid center.

Knowing the frailness of their planes, the Wrights undertook to dissuade Rodgers but finally loaned him their best mechanic, Charles Taylor. A boy mechanic named Charles S. Wiggin was also along. The party included Rodgers' young wife, Mabel, a beauty from Vermont; his mother; his manager, Fred Wettengel; and assorted Vin Fiz publicity people, a score in all.

Before the thirty-two-year-old airman and his entourage were ready, two other contestants went after the prize. Robert Fowler started eastward from San Francisco on September 11 and James Ward flew westward from Governors Island in New York Harbor on September 14, 1911. Fowler was backed by the Cole Motor Co. of Indianapolis and his plane was called the *Cole Flyer*.

Cal Rodgers' new white-winged biplane was ready for him at the Sheepshead Bay racetrack on Long Island on Sunday afternoon, September 17. It was a Wright "EX" plane weighing less than 800 pounds, with a wing spread of 32 feet and powered by a 196-pound, 35-horsepower, four-cylinder, water-cooled engine. It was a smaller form of the standard Wright "B" and could fly 55 miles an hour in calm air. The only "instrument" was a white string tied to a crosswire directly in front of the pilot to indicate the degree of climb, descent, or yawing to the right or left.

While 2,000 onlookers milled about, a young girl christened the machine with a bottle of Vin Fiz. Rodgers kissed her, accepted a freshly picked four-leaf clover from another woman, pocketed a letter from the Mayor of New York to the Mayor of San Francisco, donned his goggles and took his seat in the plane.

"Stand back or somebody will be killed!" he shouted as the two chain-driven "pusher" propellers began to whirl behind him.

His admirers fell back and at 4:22 P.M. he took off into the blue with a cigar nonchalantly clamped between his teeth. Gaining altitude, he circled over Coney Island, dropped leaflets advertising Vin Fiz, and then turned west. A million New Yorkers watched him soar over Manhattan and cross the Hudson River.

From over Jersey City, he located his special train and the Erie tracks with panels of white cloth placed between the rails to guide him out of the yards. At 5:10 P.M., he passed Paterson, N.J., where thousands had waited hours in the parks for a glimpse of him.

At 6:07 P.M., after flying 104 miles in 105 minutes, he landed for the night in a field at Middletown, N.Y., where 10,000 persons greeted him. His train arrived a few minutes later. "Well, it's a start, anyway," he noted in his log. "I get away early tomorrow at sunup."

He did, and promptly met disaster. In taking off, the plane brushed a willow tree, flopped along like a bird with a broken wing and then plunged through a big hickory tree into a chicken yard. With his cigar still in his mouth, Rodgers jumped as the plane hit the tree. It broke his fall and he was only scratched in dropping 35 feet.

But the plane was wrecked so badly that it was September 21 before he could take off in it. There was some comfort, however, in word that his rivals also had met misfortune—Robert Fowler at Colfax, Calif., and James Ward at Corning, N.Y.—and were out of the race. Earle Ovington, who had intended to compete, met with an accident at first takeoff and had also given up. But only 20 days remained before the prize deadline.

Engine trouble forced Rodgers down in a potato field near Hancock, N.Y. Repairs made, he flew on to Binghamton. Next day, he followed the wrong railroad line to Scranton, Pa., and had to fly back to Elmira, N.Y., for a net advance of only 15 miles for the day.

Serious knocks developed in the motor next day and Rodgers noticed the magneto connections were slipping out. Holding them in place with one hand, he landed in a swamp near Canisteo, N.Y. Mechanics made repairs that night but there was another forced landing next day in a meadow near Salamanca, N.Y.

"I want to fly another hundred miles before sunset," said Rodgers. In taking off, he crashed into a barbed-wire fence, was knocked unconscious, and repairs to the plane required three days. It took him 11 days to cross New York State.

He had better luck over Pennsylvania and Ohio, landing by moonlight in a pasture near Kent, Ohio. He followed the Erie Railroad to Akron, Marion, and westward. He reached Huntington, Ind., on September 30 and Hammond on October 4, despite high winds and thunderstorms.

To raise money and also to advertise the flight, the expedition went informally into the air-mail business. Only the week before, on September 23, Earle Ovington had carried the first officially authorized U.S. airplane mail from Garden City to Mineola, Long Island, about a ten-mile round trip hop. Postmaster-General Frank H. Hitchcock authorized the flight and handed Ovington a sack of specially postmarked letters.

Rodgers had no such authorization, but his young wife sold postcard pictures of the plane to the crowds at each takeoff point. For twenty-five cents each, he flew these to the next stopping point and put them into the regular mail. Each was rubber-stamped

"Carried by Rodgers Aeroplane Vin Fiz," with the date. In addition to the green one-cent government stamp showing Ben Franklin, a privately printed, black, twenty-five-cent "Rodgers Aerial Post" stamp was affixed to some. Philatelists debate the validity of this stamp but one preserved by Thomas A. Matthews of Springfield, Ohio brought $4,800 when auctioned by H. R. Harmer, Inc., on November 4, 1964, in New York.

A great Sunday crowd cheered Rodgers as he landed in Chicago's Grant Park. He and his special train continued south that afternoon to near Joliet, Ill. Next morning he circled over the penitentiary there, to the amazement of prisoners in the yard, before continuing to Peoria and Springfield, Ill.

"Rodgers Coming Fast!" headlined Missouri newspapers as he left Springfield, Ill., at 8:35 A.M. on October 10. He followed the Gulf, Mobile & Ohio tracks across the Mississippi River to land near Louisiana, Mo. Schools and business houses were closed there in his honor. Whistles were blown and church bells were rung as he landed.

He had flown farther at this point than any plane pilot in the world and was hopeful that Hearst's $50,000 offer, which expired that day, would be extended. But over the wires came word that there would be no extension. He received the news calmly when he landed at Marshall, Mo., that afternoon. His Vin Fiz contract stood; he would fly on.

Fading of hope for the $50,000 strangely enough increased public interest in Rodgers. The crowds became bigger, their cheers louder. There was something heroic about the tall, cigar-smoking man struggling on against gravity, bad luck, vagaries of the weather, and continual mechanical failure.

Whistles of all the packing houses screamed next day as he landed before a huge crowd in Swope Park in Kansas City, Mo., "to give," in the words of a local reporter, "Kansas City an aerial thrill the like of which it never had experienced before." His arrival moved a seventy-nine-year-old woman to write a poem "To Rodgers, Aviator" which concluded:

> "Sail on, brave man, from pole to pole;
> Go prove the right and might of soul!
> And may you safely reach your goal."

From Kansas City, he followed the Missouri-Kansas-Texas tracks south. The terrain was smoother, and with lapse of the prize there was no longer great pressure to go west. There also were fairs that gave Rodgers opportunity for extra money and a chance for the Vin Fiz people to obtain some visual publicity with the crowds. While newspapers reported the flight, most made no mention of the sponsor. In many places only those who saw the plane or train read about Vin Fiz.

Rodgers had the best day's flying of his trip in making the 189 miles from Kansas City to Vinita, Okla., with two stops. He continued on through Muskogee and McAlester to Fort Worth, Tex., and then over to the Texas State Fair at Dallas, where he did some stunts for a crowd of 75,000. He flew on south by way of Waxahachie, Hillsboro, and Waco. Every whistle in these towns tooted for him. He circled the 311-foot dome of the State Capitol at Austin on October 20, but had a serious accident that day a few miles south at Kyle, Tex.

"Rodgers nearly met his death while in the air at 3,500 feet," logged his staff. "Crystallized piston and intake valves nearly made a wreck. The aviator shut off his engine, volplaned two miles, and made a perfect landing in the only pasture within 40 miles."

Two days later, he landed at San Antonio on the polo field of Fort Sam Houston in the midst of a crowd so large that mounted cavalrymen had to keep order. After two days' rest, he turned west over the Southern Pacific tracks and came down for the night near Spofford Junction in a road where a cactus thorn ripped one of his tires.

Next day brought another accident. One propeller hit something and swerved the biplane into a barbed-wire fence. "This is just a small wreck," Rodgers assured the crowd as he climbed out.

Repairs made, he flew next day to Del Rio, Dryden, and Sanderson, Tex., making 174 miles in 140 minutes. He followed the Rio Grande and at times flew over Mexico.

While 2,000 feet above Fort Hancock, he noticed his water pump leaking. It soon began to steam. Rodgers attempted to glide to a plowed field but came down in a mesquite thicket and smashed a landing skid. It was replaced and he flew to El Paso that afternoon in time to be taken to the Sunday bull fight in Juarez. But when the matador moved in for the kill, the dauntless airman turned away. "I can't watch it," he explained. "It would just make me sick."

Motor trouble forced him down at Deming, N. Mex., but he flew over the Continental Divide and reached Tucson, Ariz., on November 1. There he shook hands with his rival, Robert Fowler, who had resumed his flight east and who eventually became the first airman to cross the country from west to east. After several stops in the Arizona desert, Rodgers flew his battered, much-repaired plane into California from Stovall, Ariz.

While flying 4,000 feet above the Salton Sea, the No. 1 cylinder of the motor exploded without warning. Steel splinters shot into Rodgers' right arm. As the engine died, oil splattered over his goggles, blinding him. But the airman coolly ripped them off and with his left hand brought the plane down in the desert almost without a scratch. Young Wiggin labored two days in the blazing sun to assemble a new engine from parts of two others.

Rodgers took off again for a hair-raising experience in rugged, windswept San Gorgonio Pass. The magneto connections began to work loose as the plane was flying 5,000 feet above the canyon's rocky floor. Then a connecting rod broke. Oil began to spurt. But Rodgers miraculously landed the plane in an alfalfa field near Banning, Calif.

After more repairs, he took off on Sunday, November 5, stopped for gasoline at Pomona, and landed in triumph before 10,000 cheering enthusiasts at Pasadena. Over a special telephone line, he laconically reported to the Associated Press his arrival at Tournament Park. Pretty girls gave him chrysanthemums. An American flag was draped about him and he was driven around the race course in an automobile.

He had crossed America in 49 days and survived 16 crashes.

Offered anything he liked at the Maryland Hotel that night, Rodgers said, "I'd like some crackers and a glass of milk." The next day he visited a high school where students gave him more flowers and crowned him with a laurel wreath.

The Vin Fiz people called the trip completed and dismissed the special train. The venture had cost them about $180,000 and most Americans still were drinking Coca-Cola. But Rodgers wanted to fly the few remaining miles to the Pacific and was offered a purse to do so at Long Beach. He contracted to fly the following Sunday, November 12, and, though local ministers protested, felt that he could not disappoint the waiting crowd.

His engine stopped soon after he took off and he landed near Eastlake to discover a fuel line broken. This was soldered at a neighboring farm house and he again took to the air. Fifteen minutes later something else went wrong and the biplane crashed on a ranch a mile southeast of Compton.

It was a serious accident. Rodgers hit the ground head first, suffered a brain concussion, a smashed ankle and gasoline burns. The canny owner of the ranch exacted $10 damage for the trampling of his field before he allowed the wrecked plane to be removed.

Finally, on December 10, the now crippled airman tied his crutches to the battered plane and again took off for the Pacific. With the inevitable cigar in his mouth, he landed gracefully 16 minutes later at the foot of Linden Avenue in Long Beach to the cheers of 40,000, including his wife and mother.

After local notables formally rolled the wheels of the biplane into the water, one said: "Too bad about the $50,000."

"Money isn't everything!" retorted Rodgers. "I made it, didn't I?"

It was well that he thought so. From his various sponsors, Rodgers had received about $22,000 but he had spent more than

$20,000. Of the original plane, only the vertical rudder and drip pan remained. Everything else had been replaced. Eight propellers had been used.

Rodgers had flown 4,321 miles, more than three times that of any other flyer. But he had actually been in the air only 82 hours and figured that he had averaged 51.59 miles an hour. His longest single hop had been the 137 miles from Stovall, Ariz., to Imperial Junction, Calif. The Aero Club of America gave him its gold medal.

"Thirty days is too short now for a flight from coast to coast," he told a newspaperman. "But I expect to see the time when we shall be carrying passengers in flying machines from New York to the Pacific Coast in three days. That is an average of more than 100 miles an hour, and cannot be done until some way is devised to box in the passengers as the wind tears one awfully at such speed as that."

His prediction was realized but Rodgers did not live to see it. A few months later, on April 3, 1912, the airman went stunting for another Sunday crowd at Long Beach. He dipped close to a roller coaster and then dived under a flock of sea gulls. At a height of 200 feet, he was seen to take his hands off the controls.

The biplane plunged into knee-deep water almost at the exact spot where he had ended his transcontinental trip. His neck was broken and Calbraith Perry Rodgers, descendant of Navy heroes, died as rescuers carried him from the water.

He was the 127th person to be killed in an airplane accident. The first had been Lt. Thomas E. Selfridge of the Army, fatally hurt as a passenger in a plane being demonstrated by Orville Wright at Ft. Myer, Va., in 1908. Selfridge Field is named for him. Cal Rodgers' cousin, John, rose to Commander in the Navy, served with distinction in World War I, established the Naval Air Station at San Diego, and commanded the one in Pearl Harbor. In 1925, he led the first Navy seaplane flight from California to Hawaii, making the last 450 miles on water when gasoline was exhausted. Like his cousin, he was fatally hurt in a crash, and died

August 27, 1926, in the hospital at the League Island Navy Yard, Philadelphia, Pa.

Fifty years after Cal Rodgers' epic flight, the Federal Aviation Agency formally designated the route that he followed as a skyway bearing his name. Attending the Washington ceremonies in connection with this on July 10, 1961, were Cal Rodgers' widow and the late Charles S. Wiggin, who had been his boy mechanic. They married after the airman's death and for some years resided in Westport, Conn., and, at the time of Mr. Wiggin's death, November 8, 1964, in Miami, Fla.

The historic *Vin Fiz Flyer* was repaired and given to the Carnegie Museum in Pittsburgh, where the airman had been born. This institution presented the biplane to the National Air Museum of the Smithsonian Institution in Washington, D.C. It is displayed there today not far from the original Wright airplane. Nearby are the *Spirit of St. Louis,* in which Charles Lindbergh flew to Paris, and the *Winnie Mae,* in which Wiley Post circled the globe.

JOHN D. MAC DONALD

The Big Blue

I WALKED DOWN THE LENGTH of the curved concrete pier at Acapulco, passing the charter boats getting ready to take off across the
sparkling blue morning water after the sail and the marlin.

Pedro Martinez, skipper of the shabby-looking Orizaba, was
standing on the pier coiling a line. I have gone out many times
with Pedro during the season for the past five years. Other craft
are prettier, but Pedro's equipment is good, and he knows where
the fish can be found. Pedro did not look happy. Not at all.

Lew Wolta sat in one of the two stern fishing chairs half under
the canopy. He looked up at me, waved the half-empty bottle of
beer in his big hand, and said, "What the hell kept you, Thompson?"

I had met Wolta the afternoon before. He and his friend, Jimmy
Gerran, had stepped up to Pedro to sew him up for the next day
at the same time I did. We had joined forces. I knew that Wolta
had wanted the Orizaba because he had seen the four flags flying
and the hard, lean, black bodies of the two sails on the tiny deck
forward of the cabin.

When we had gone across the street to seal the bargain over a
beer, I had begun to regret my quick decision. Wolta was a tall,

hard, heavy-shouldered man in his late thirties with a huge voice, white teeth gleaming in a constant grin, and washed-out eyes that never smiled at all. He kept up a running chatter, most of which seemed designed to inflict hurt on the younger, frailer Jimmy Gerran, a quiet lad with a humble manner.

Over the beer, Wolta said, "Yeah, I ran into Jimmy up in Taxco, and it was pretty obvious that he needed somebody to get him out of his daze. Hell, I've never been in this gook country before, but I've got a nose for fun. Leave Jimmy alone and he'd spend all his time walking around the streets."

At that he had slapped Gerran roughly on the shoulder. "To-morrow we hook a sail, boy, and it'll make a man out of you."

Pedro stepped down onto the fantail, and I handed him my lunch and equipment. Pedro said, in quick, slurred Spanish, "This man talks to me, Señor Thompson, as if I were his gardener."

"What did he say?" Wolta asked suspiciously.

"He said that he thinks we'll have a good day."

"That's fine!" Wolta said, his eyes still holding a glint of mistrust. "How'd you learn this language?"

"I live here," I said shortly. "Where's Gerran?"

"I sent Jimmy after cigarettes. Hope he can find his way back to the boat. Here he comes now."

Jimmy gave me a shy smile and said good morning as he climbed down into the boat. Pedro's two hands were aboard—his engineer and his sailor. The sailor went forward and got the anchor line. The marine engine chuckled deeply as Pedro moved ahead away from the dock. We were about fifth or sixth away from the dock.

Wolta examined the heavy boat rods curiously. He fingered the gimbal set into the front of the chair. He said, "You set the rod butt in this thing, eh? Universal joint."

Jimmy said, "I've never done this before. What happens, Mr. Thompson?"

"You sit and hold the rod. Your bait, a fish about eight inches long with the hook sewed into it, will ride the surface about fifty feet astern. See, the sailor's dropping the bamboo outriggers now.

The line will run taut from your bait to a heavy clothespin at the tip of the outrigger. Then there'll be twenty or so feet of slack between the clothespin and the tip of your rod. The sail'll come up and whack the fish with his bill. That's to kill it. It'll knock the line out of the clothespin, and the fish will lie dead on the water while we keep moving. Then the sail'll grab it. As soon as the slack is all gone, hold tight and hit him three or four times. Not hard. Like this." I took the rod and showed him.

"How will I know if he's hooked?" Jimmy asked.

Wolta roared. "He'll rise up and talk to you, boy. He'll come up and tell you all about it."

Jimmy flushed. He said, "Thanks, Mr. Thompson."

I was assembling my equipment. For sail I use a five-foot, five-ounce tip, 4/0 star drag reel carrying five hundred yards of 6-thread, 18-pound test line. Wolta looked on curiously. He said, "That's a lot lighter outfit than these, Thompson." I nodded. The boat rods carry 32-thread line, 14/0 drag reels. Wolta said, "That rod won't fit in the gimbal, will it?"

"No," I said shortly.

Wolta frowned. "What the hell! If you can use that stuff, why should we fish with rope and crowbars?"

I said, "If you never fished for sail before and if you hooked one with this equipment, you'd have a thousand to one chance of bringing him in. He'd break your line or your tip every time."

Wolta gave me that grin. "I guess you know what you're talking about," he said.

The bait was all sewed. It was taken off the ice, and Pedro helped rig the lines. As soon as we rounded the headlands, the bait went out. I said, "You two fish. As soon as you've hooked one, the other man reels in. Fast. I'll take the place of whoever hooks the first one."

"Hooks or catches," Wolta said suspiciously.

I looked him squarely in the eyes. "Hooks!" I said.

"Okay, okay," he mumbled, turning away. I had learned something interesting about Lew Wolta.

The first half hour was dull. Pedro headed straight out, and the shore line began to recede; the dusty brown hills began to appear behind the green hills that encircle Acapulco. The swell was heavy. I watched both Jimmy and Wolta and saw with relief that neither of them seemed conscious of the movement of the boat. A seasick man aboard spoils my pleasure in the day, as I know how badly he wants to return to the stability of the land.

The bait danced and skittered astern, taking off into the air at the crest of the waves, sometimes going under the surface for a dozen yards.

Wolta called for more beer and called loudly again as the sailor was uncapping the bottle.

The engineer, acting as lookout, yelled and pointed. Pedro took a quick look and heeled the boat around. The sail was a dust brown shape dimly seen a few inches under the surge of the blue sea.

We dragged the bait by him, and he seemed to shake himself, move in a big circle, come in on the bait with arrowlike speed. He was headed for Gerran's bait. For a moment the sail knifed the water a few yards behind the bait and then there was a boiling spot on the flank of a wave and the line snapped out of Gerran's clothespin.

I watched the line tauten as Pedro cut speed.

"Now!" I said.

Jimmy hit him just a shade late, but hit him with the right force. The line whined out of the reel as the sail, about seventy pounds of angry, startled temper, walked up into the air, three feet of daylight showing under his bullet-lean tail.

Jimmy gasped. The sail jumped high again, ten yards farther. High in the air he shook his head, and we saw the bait snap free and fall out in a long arc. The fish was off the hook and, somewhere under the surface of the sea, he was heading for distant parts.

There was that letdown of tension that always comes with a lost fish.

"Absolutely beautiful!" Jimmy said softly.

Wolta gave his hoarse laugh. "Absolutely butterfingered, pal. You had him and you lost him."

"I've never seen anything like that," Jimmy said.

"I'd have liked to see him boated," Wolta said. "What the hell good is it to look at a fish?"

Pedro smiled at Jimmy and said, in his thick English, "Bad luck. Next time you get heem." Then he turned to Wolta. "You reel in too slow, meester. Faster next time, eh?"

Wolta, smiling, said, "You run your boat, pop. I'll reel in like I damn well please."

I threw my bait out over the side toward the stern. I was learning about Wolta. I said in Spanish to Pedro, "This one is all mouth, my friend." I said to Wolta, "I just told him that if I hook a fish, he's to cut your line if you don't bring it in fast enough."

Wolta said, "Okay, okay. Don't get in a sweat, Thompson."

I sat down. I had the drag off, my thumb on the spool. Jimmy said, behind me, "You don't use the clothespin?"

"No. When I get a strike, I let the line run free, then throw on the drag when I hit him. It's harder to do it right this way, but when you get onto it, you can figure the time to fit the way each fish hits."

Wolta said, a faint sneer in his tone, "Don't bother the expert, Jimmy."

I let that one pass.

Ten minutes later Wolta said, "I hear it takes about a half hour, forty minutes to boat one with the equipment I'm using. How long does it take with your rig?"

"Longer. Maybe an hour with the same size fish."

He still wore the smile. He said, "That's great! I pay a third of the boat the same as you and then when you hook one, I got to stop fishing for an hour."

"That's right," I said mildly.

Pedro had reached the area he liked. He began to zig-zag back and forth across the area. The Spanish word for that maneuver is, very neatly, the same as the Spanish word for eel.

I was first to see the fish coming in toward Wolta's bait. I said, "One coming up." Pedro slowed a little as Wolta tensed. It was as unreasonable as any sailfish. It cut by Wolta's bait and, instead of hitting mine first to kill it, it gulped it whole. It was one very hungry fish. I hit it immediately.

When it jumped, I saw that it was probably a shade smaller than the one Jimmy had hooked. As it ran I saw Wolta reeling in rapidly.

Any sailfish could find freedom if it had the sense to run on a straight line, take all the line, break the line at the end of the run. But five hundred yards is a long way to go in a straight line. I stood in front of the chair. When it jumped, I kept the line taut, pulling it off balance, slapping it down against the sea before it could shake its head.

It headed for the Orient; then, as I was getting worried about the line, it began to cut around in a vast circle, and I won back a little line. It stopped jumping. Bringing in the line was the usual tough problem. A hundred yards from the boat and twenty minutes later it walked on its tail for a good dozen yards and then, as I had expected, it sounded. I horsed it up, a few feet at a time. It made one more jump close to the boat and then came in, dog weary. Pedro handled the gaff. The sailor grasped the bill, and Pedro belted it across the back of the neck with the weighted club.

The sail came in over the transom, glistening with a hundred impossibly beautiful iridescent colors. Jimmy squatted and watched the colors slowly fade until the fish became the usual shining gunmetal black of the dead sail. He turned glowing eyes up toward me and said, "That was wonderful!"

"The experts are always wonderful," Wolta said. He grinned at me. "Do I have your permission to fish?"

He got his line in first. Fresh bait was put on the other line, and Jimmy took his place in the chair. It was not over five minutes later that a sail, without warning, came up from downstairs and slapped Wolta's bait. I was behind his chair. He waited the proper time until the line straightened and then hit, much too hard. But it didn't do any harm because he wasn't hitting against the fish. The sail was waiting longer than usual.

Instinctively I reached down over Wolta's shoulder and released the drag so the spool would run free, allowing the bait to remain dead on the water.

Wolta pushed my hand away hard, saying in a tight voice, "Catch your own fish, Doc."

It was a comedy of errors. The fish took the bait, and then Wolta tried to hit it with the drag off and without his thumb on the spool. The spool whined and the line snarled. Pedro came running and grasped the line ahead of the rod and yanked hard three times, setting the hook. The fish went high. It was one fine sail. I guessed it as close to ninety pounds. The world's record is 106 pounds off Miami in 1929. Pedro managed to click the drag back on and ripped at the snarled line while the sail jumped wildly, lashing, fighting.

With the snarl gone, the fish hit the end of the slack with a jar that made Wolta grunt and yanked his arms straight, yanked the rod tip down. When the fish jumped again, Wolta horsed it so hard that he spun the sail in the air.

I yelled at him, "You'll bust the line!"

He worked with a tight hard grin on his face. The sail took line on him, but took it with the full drag and with Wolta's hard thumb on the spool. I don't know why the line didn't break. It would test at 96 pounds.

I'll say this for Wolta. He was a powerful man. Cords like cables stood out on his brown forearms as he horsed the fish toward the boat. Pedro began to look worried. Even boating a tired fish is rugged work. Last year, just as a man reached for the bill, the fish took one more leap, freeing himself of the gaff. The bill entered the brain of the sailor through his left eye. And Pedro saw himself trying to boat a fish that still had a lot of fight left.

Pedro worked the boat, turning it perfectly, keeping it so that Wolta had free play of the fish. The fish made short hard savage lunges close to the boat. Pedro left the wheel, handled the gaff himself, sunk it neatly. The fish gave a convulsive heave that nearly lifted Pedro over the side. The sailor went half over the rail, grasped the bill with his gloved hand, and slammed the fish twice behind the eyes. Pedro heaved it aboard.

The fish lay there. Reflex muscles made it quiver. Wolta grabbed the club from the sailor and hit it again. It was an understandable thing to do. But the way he did it, the way the club smashed against the hard flesh, revealed something savage and soul-naked about the man. Pedro looked disgusted.

Wolta turned to me and said, "I got it in spite of you. Next time keep your damn hands off my rod and reel, mister."

I said, "Wake up, Wolta. If I hadn't thrown off the drag, you wouldn't even have a fish. He didn't have the bait when you hit him. I let the bait free so that it stayed back there. You kept me from putting the drag back on. That's why your line snarled."

He smiled at me. His pale eyes still held anger. "If you say so, expert. Anyway, this one will outweigh yours." He kicked the dead fish. I didn't like that, and neither did Pedro. A sail is an honorable opponent, a brave fish, a gentleman of the sea. Even dead he isn't to be kicked.

"It probably will," I said.

We had the two flags up for the two sails. I took Wolta's place while he went inside to have another beer. I had noticed that his thumb was raw where he had pressed it against the escaping line.

Jimmy Gerran dropped his bait back into the water. Wolta hollered out, "Both the *men* have got a fish, kid. Now let's see if you can lose another one." He laughed hugely. Jimmy smiled weakly. I smiled not at all.

We fished without result for over an hour and then we ate. Even without another strike, it would have been a good day. But I was pulling for Jimmy to latch onto one. And I had a hunch that when he did, he'd do a better job than Wolta had. Only Wolta seemed oblivious of the fact that enormous luck had kept his line from snapping.

We were out a good dozen miles, and the sun was almost directly overhead, making a dazzling glare on the blue sea.

The time went by slowly. Wolta said, "Somebody catch something. I want some more fishing." He waited a few minutes. He said, "Jimmy, if you don't have anything by three o'clock. I'm taking over."

I said, "Don't you think we ought to stick to the rules?"

"Okay, Jimmy?" Wolta said. "Three o'clock?"

Jimmy didn't look at me. He said, "Sure, Lew."

The older man had him buffaloed. I knew the signs. I liked Gerran. So all I could do was to think that it was just too bad.

While I was wondering how Gerran got himself tied up with Wolta, Pedro hissed and said in Spanish, "There is a monstrous fish to starboard, señor."

I searched the sea until I saw it. It was too close. There wasn't time for me to reel in and change to the boat rod. This fish wasn't going to be brought in on my tackle.

For a moment I had a yen to try for him, anyway. But I reeled in quickly.

Wolta said, "What's up? Why're you reeling in?"

At first the sun was in my eyes. And then I saw him coming in like a freight train. He slapped Jimmy's bait out of the water. It fell dead, free of the clothespin, and the fish took it. Jimmy hit it perfectly, four times. The huge fish was on his way out to sea when he felt a nasty little jab inside his jaw. He felt a jab and a tugging weight. To free himself of it, he went upstairs. He went up in a shower of spray—five hundred pounds of blue marlin.

Wolta yelled in astonishment. A wide grin split Pedro's face. The hands gabbled in excitement. There aren't many fish like that one off Acapulco. Jimmy didn't give him any slack when he jumped again and again. Then the big blue headed for off and beyond, and the reel sang a high shrill song of irresistible power.

Jimmy should have been using a thirty-ounce tip, a 16/o reel and 54-thread line. In relation to the blue, his tackle was as relatively light as mine was for sail. Jimmy held the rod and gave us one taut, startled look as Pedro and I grabbed the straps and strapped him to the chair.

The reel continued to sing, and the line going into the water was a white hissing streak. I began to pray to Aztec gods for the big fish to get tired of that straight line. Pedro was back at the wheel. He jammed it into reverse and backed along the line of flight of the fish. The powersong diminished in pitch a few notes, but still the monster drove on, trying to run from the pain in his jaw. He made a leap a full fifteen hundred feet from the boat. He was so far away that he looked like a minnow. Pedro stopped backing instantly to keep from piling up slack.

Jimmy began to pull on the fish. It was going at right angles to the boat. Pedro kept the boat in a small turn to keep the fish centered over the stern. With both hands on the rod, Jimmy pulled slowly, pulling the rod from a horizontal to a vertical position. Then, as he lowered it quickly, he reeled in a few feet of the precious line. It was heartbreakingly slow compared to the speed at which it had gone out. Fifty times he strained to pull up on the rod, gaining a few feet each time, and then the fish, undiminished in power, took it all away from him again.

We were covering a lot of ground. Every time the fish took off, Pedro would keep after it, conserving that precious line. Once the spool showed as the fish stopped his run and jumped.

I glanced at my wristwatch. Forty minutes so far. The sweat poured off Jimmy Gerran, and his shirt looked as though he had been doused with a bucket of water. I kept encouraging him in low tones. I knew what the fight was taking out of him. Heave up and reel in, heave up and reel in. Minute after minute.

Then the fish came like an express train, right for the boat, its miniature sail cutting the water. The line came fast then. It passed the boat within fifty feet and went on out in the opposite direction. I was afraid of what would happen when it hit the end of the temporary slack. Jimmy was smart enough to stop reeling and wait, rod level. The spool jumped from complete stillness into whining speed as the line went out. But this time the fish turned and tail-walked some three hundred yards from the boat.

Once again the laborious process began. When I saw the blood on Jimmy's wrist I knew what the blisters were doing to his hands. His face was set and death-pale, and there was more blood on his lower lip.

Wolta sat in the other chair and said in a wheedling voice, "Kid, you're bushed. You're not tough enough for that baby. Next time you get a chance, slip the rod over here. Old Lew'll bring him in for you."

The kid didn't answer, but he didn't seem to be working so hard on the fish. I know the feeling. I've been hooked into fish who have almost convinced me that it is impossible to bring them in.

Yet he worked on, his arms trembling each time he pulled. I looked at my watch. An hour and fifteen minutes of heartbreaking, muscle-ripping, back-bending labor.

"Come on, Jimmy. Hand it over," Wolta said. I wanted to tell him to shut his face. But it was the kid's problem, not mine.

Jimmy began to rest for little intervals when he could have been regaining line. But the big marlin wasn't as eager as he had been. He was fighting doggedly, but without that first, wild, reckless speed.

Wolta said, "Tell you what. I'll slip into your chair and you slip out. Take the rod butt out of the gimmick just long enough to slip your leg under."

Jimmy made no objection. I moved back. Wolta came over and began to fumble with the buckle on one of the straps. Jimmy sat without trying to regain line.

The fish was about a hundred and seventy yards out. Suddenly his first fury seemed to come back to him and the fish shot out of the water at an angle, covering what seemed to be twenty yards in a straight line, leaning up out of the water at an angle, dancing on his tail, lashing the sea to foam with his enormous tail.

I saw Jimmy's hands tight on the rod, saw the dried blood on his wrist. "Lay off, Wolta," he said thickly, hardly speaking above a whisper.

Wolta laughed his great gusty laugh and continued to work on the buckle. Jimmy told him to lay off again. Wolta paid no attention and only said, "I can bring that big baby in."

The fish was taking out line slowly. Jimmy took his right hand off the rod butt, swung it in a short hard arc. His fist hit Wolta in the mouth. Wolta took two stumbling steps back and sat down hard. Jimmy didn't even look around. He began to fight back a few feet of line at a time. Wolta got up with a roar deep in his throat. For once that mechanical smile was gone from his bruised lips. He started toward Jimmy, big fists clenched.

The sailor, a hundred-and-twenty-pound Mexican with dark soft eyes, suddenly appeared between Jimmy and Wolta. He looked mildly at Wolta, and his hand was on the haft of his belt knife. Wolta stopped as though he had run into a wall.

He gave me a mechanical smile and said, "Okay, okay. Let the kid lose the fish."

Jimmy labored on. He looked as though he would keel over from exhaustion, sag unconscious in the harness. But somewhere he found the strength to match the wild courage of the fish.

One hundred and fifty yards. One hundred and twenty. One hundred. And he had been on the fish for over two hours. When the fish was within seventy feet of the boat, it spun and went on out again, but not more than a hundred yards. I heard Jimmy's harsh sob as he began once more to bring it in. The marlin sounded, going down two hundred feet, lying there like a stone. Jimmy brought it up, foot by foot. The blue came up the last thirty feet at enormous speed and shot high into the air, seeming to hang over the boat for an instant, living beauty against the deep blue of the sky. When it hit the water, the spray shot up against us.

It came in slowly from twenty yards, lolling in the water, rolling to show its belly, all fight suddenly gone.

Two hours and forty-three minutes. Pedro gaffed it and it was

killed and the sailor with a line around him went down into the
sea and got a line on the fish, got a firm loop around the waist of
the tail.

Wolta had to be asked to get on the line with us. Jimmy sagged
limply in the harness, his eyes half closed, his hands hanging limp.
A heavy drop of blood fell from the palm of his hand to the deck.
We got the monster over the side. It was the biggest blue I had
ever seen. Not record of course. Record is 737 pounds, Bimini,
1919.

Wolta made no sound of praise. Phlegmatic Pedro forgot himself so far as to pound Jimmy on his tired back with a brown fist,
saying, "Muy hombre! Muy hombre!"

Literally translated it means, "Very man." But the sense is, "You
are one hell of a man!"

We unstrapped Jimmy, and I actually had to help him in to the
bunk. He gave me a weak, tired grin. We headed in.

Wolta said, "How about letting me fish on the way in."

Pedro said, "Too late, meester."

Wolta said, "Lot of fishing I got today. Just about one damn
hour."

"You got yourself a big sail," I said.

The blue dwarfed our two sail. Wolta snorted and went and got
a beer out of the ice locker.

Boating the blue should have been the high point of the day.
Or even that punch in the mouth. But it wasn't.

The high point came after we were on the pier. We were the
last boat in. Dusk was coming. A man waits near the pier by the
big scaffolding where they hang up the fish. He takes pictures,
good pictures, for a moderate fee.

The crowd was beginning to drift away. They came back in a
hurry when the big blue was hauled up onto the pier. They came
back and gasped and gabbled and asked questions.

Wolta answered the questions. Wolta stuck out his chest.
Though he didn't have the nerve to say so, he answered the questions in such a way that the crowd was led to believe that it was
his fish.

The line was thrown over the scaffolding and it took four men to haul the blue clear of the ground. Pedro brought the rods up, leaned them against the side of the scaffolding. The blue was in the middle with the two sails on either side.

The man had his camera set up. I wasn't interested in being in a picture with Wolta. The crowd got back out of the line of the picture. Wolta put his heavy arm on Jimmy's shoulder and said to the crowd at large, "Tomorrow the kid and I are going out and get another one." And he laughed.

Somehow he had edged over so that he was closer to the blue than Jimmy was. I smiled wryly as I thought of Wolta showing copies of the picture to his friends.

Jimmy said tightly, "Hold it!" He held up his hand. The photographer ducked out from under his black cloth looking puzzled.

Jimmy shrugged Wolta's arm off his shoulder. He said, "Wolta, we aren't going out tomorrow or any other day. Together. And suppose you have your own picture taken with your own fish and get the hell away from mine!"

The crowd was hushed and expectant. A woman giggled. Wolta looked pale and dangerous. He said, "Kid, you shouldn't talk that way to me. I'm warning you!"

Jimmy doubled one of his torn hands and said, "Move off!"

Wolta slowly relaxed. "Okay, okay. If that's the way you want it." He went off into the crowd.

Jimmy looked directly at me and said, "Mr. Thompson, I'd like you in this picture and Pedro and the other two men."

I spoke to Pedro. We stepped into the picture.

Just before the camera clicked, I glanced at Jimmy beside me. Tears of anger still stood in his eyes, but his chin was up and he was smiling.

I still have the picture. It's before me right now. And when I look at the expression on Jimmy's face, I'm reminded of the expressions I saw on many faces several years ago. . . .

The faces of the men when we dropped out of the sky into that prison camp in the Philippines and liberated them.

AVRAM DAVIDSON

The Cobblestones of
Saratoga Street

"COBBLESTONES TO GO," SAID THE HEADLINE. Miss Louisa lifted her eyebrows, lifted her quizzing-glass (probably the last one in actual use anywhere in the world), read the article, passed it to her sister. Miss Augusta read it without eyeglass or change of countenance, and handed it back.

"They shan't," she said.

They glanced at a faded photograph in a silver frame on the mantelpiece, then at each other. Miss Louisa placed the newspaper next to the pewter chocolate-pot, tinkled a tiny bell. After a moment a white-haired colored man entered the room.

"Carruthers," said Miss Augusta, "you may clear away breakfast."

"Well, *I* think it is outrageous," Betty Linkhorn snapped.

"My dear," her grandfather said mildly, "you can't stop progress." He sipped his tea.

"Progress my eye! This is the only decently paved street in the whole town—you know that, don't you, Papa? Just because it's cobblestone and not concrete—or macadam—or—"

"My dear," said Edward Linkhorn, "I remember when several

88

of the streets were still paved with wood. I remember it quite particularly because, in defiance of my father's orders, I went barefoot one fine summer's day and got a splinter in my heel. My mother took it out with a needle and my father thrashed me. . . . Besides, don't you find the cobblestones difficult to manage in high-heeled shoes?"

Betty smiled—not sweetly. "I don't find them difficult at all. Mrs. Harris does—but, then, if *she'd* been thrashed for going barefoot. . . . Come on, Papa," she said, while her grandfather maintained a diplomatic silence, "admit it—if Mrs. Harris hadn't sprained her ankle, if her husband wasn't a paving contractor, if his partner wasn't C. B. Smith, the state chairman of the party that's had the city, county, *and* state sewn up for twenty years—"

Mr. Linkhorn spread honey on a small piece of toast. " 'If wishes were horses, beggars would ride—' "

"Well, what's wrong with that?"

" '—and all mankind be consumed with pride.' My dear, I will see what I can do."

His Honor was interviewing the press. "Awright, what's next? New terlets in the jail, right? Awright, if them bums and smokies wouldn't of committed no crimes they wouldn't be in no jail, right? Awright, what's next? Cobblestones? *Cobblestones?* Damn it, *again* this business wit the cobblestones! You'd think they were diamonds or sumpthin'. Aw*right.* Well, om, look, except for Saratoga Street, the last cobblestones inna city were tore up when I was a *boy,* for Pete's sake. Allathem people there, they're living inna past, yaknowwhatimean? Allathem gas lamps in frunna the houses, huh? Hitching posts and carriage blocks, for Pete sakes! Whadda they think we're living inna horse-and-buggy age? *Awright,* they got that park with a fence around it, private property, okay. But the streets belong to the City, see? Somebody breaks a leg on wunna them cobblestones, they can *sue* the City, right? So—*cobblestones?* Up they come, anats all there is to it. Awright, what's next?"

His comments appeared in the newspaper (the publisher of which knew what side his Legal Advertisements were buttered on) in highly polished form. *I yield to no one in my respect for tradition and history, but the cobblestoned paving of Saratoga Street is simply too dangerous to be endured. The cobblestones will be replaced by a smooth, efficient surface more in keeping with the needs of the times.*

As the Mayor put it, "What's next?"

Next was a series of protests by the local, county, and state historical societies, all of which protests were buried in two- or three-line items in the back of the newspaper. But (as the publisher put it, "After all, C.B., business is business. And, besides, it won't make any difference in the long run, anyway.") the Saratoga Street Association reprinted them in a full-page advertisement headed PROTECT OUR HERITAGE, and public interest began to pick up.

It was stimulated by the interest shown in the metropolitan papers, all of which circulated locally. BLUEBLOODS MAN THE BARRICADES, said one. 20TH CENTURY CATCHES UP WITH SARATOGA STREET, said another. BELOVED COBBLESTONES DOOMED, HISTORICAL SARATOGA STREET PREPARES TO SAY FAREWELL, lamented a third. And so it went.

And it also went like this: *To The Editor, Sir, I wish to point out an error in the letter which claimed that the cobblestones were laid down in 1836. True, the houses in Saratoga Street were mostly built in that year, but like many local streets it was not paved at all until late in the '90s. So the cobblestones are not so old as some people think.*

And it went like this, too:

Mr. Edward Linkhorn: Would you gentlemen care for anything else to drink?

Reporter: Very good whiskey.

Photographer: Very good.

Linkhorn: We are very gratified that a national picture magazine is giving us so much attention.

Reporter: Well, *you* know—human interest story. Not so much soda, Sam.

Photographer: Say, Mr. Linkhorn, can I ask you a question?

Linkhorn: Certainly.

Photographer: Well, I notice that on all the houses—in all the windows, I mean—they got these signs, *Save Saratoga Street Cobblestones*. All but one house. How come? They *against* the stones?

Reporter: Say, that's right, Mr. Linkhorn. How come—?

Linkhorn: Well, gentlemen, that house, number 25, belongs to the Misses de Gray.

Reporter: de Gray? de Gray?

Linkhorn: Their father was General de Gray of Civil War fame. His statue is in de Gray Square. We also have a de Gray Avenue.

Reporter: His *daughters* are still living? What are they like?

Linkhorn: I have never had the privilege of meeting them.

Miss Adelaide Tallman's family was every bit as good as any of those who lived on Saratoga Street; the Tallmans had simply never *cared* to live on Saratoga Street, that was all. The Tallman estate had been one of the sights of the city, but nothing remained of it now except the name *Jabez Tallman* on real estate maps used in searching land titles, and the old mansion itself—much modified now, and converted into a funeral parlor. Miss Tallman herself lived in a nursing home. Excitement was rare in her life, and she had no intention of passing up any bit of attention which came her way.

"I knew the de Gray girls well," she told the lady from the news syndicate. This was a big fib; she had never laid eyes on them in her life—but who was to know? She had *heard* enough about them to talk as if she had, and if the de Gray girls didn't like it, let them come and tell her so. Snobby people, the de Grays, always were. What if her father, Mr. Tallman, *had* hired a substitute during the Rebellion? *Hmph.*

"Oh, they were the most beautiful things! Louisa was the older, she was blonde. Augusta's hair was brown. They always had plenty of beaux—not that I didn't have my share of them too, mind you," she added, looking sharply at the newspaper lady, as if daring her to deny it. "But nobody was ever good enough for *them*. There was one young man, his name was Horace White, and—oh, he was the *handsomest* thing! I danced with him myself," she said complacently, "at the Victory Ball after the Spanish War. He had gone away to be an officer in the Navy, and he was just the most handsome thing in his uniform that you ever saw. But *he* wasn't good enough for them, either. He went away after that—went out west to Chicago or some such place—and no one ever heard from him again. Jimmy Taylor courted Augusta, and William Snow and Rupert Roberts—no, Rupert was sweet on Louisa, yes, but—"

The newspaper lady asked when Miss Tallman had last seen the de Gray sisters.

Oh, said Miss Tallman vaguely, many years ago. *Many* years ago. . . . (Had she really danced with anybody at the Victory Ball? Was she still wearing her hair down then? Perhaps she was thinking of the Junior Cotillion. Oh, well, who was to know?)

"About 1905," she said firmly, crossing her fingers under her blanket. "But, you see, nobody was *good* enough for them. And so, by and by, they stopped seeing *anybody*. And that's the way it was."

That was not quite the way it was. They saw Carruthers.

Carruthers left the house on Sunday mornings only—to attend services at the A.M.E. Zion Church. Sunday evenings he played the harmonium while Miss Louisa and Miss Augusta sang hymns. All food was delivered and Carruthers received it either at the basement door or the rear door. The Saratoga Street Association took care of the maintenance of the outside of the house, of course;

all Carruthers had to do there was sweep the walk and polish the brass.

It must not be thought that because his employers were recluses, Carruthers was one, too; or because they did not choose to communicate with the outside world, he did not choose to do so, either. If, while engaged in his chores, he saw people he knew, he would greet them. He was, in fact, the first person to greet Mrs. Henry Harris when she moved into Saratoga Street.

"Why, hel-lo, Henrietta," he said. "What in the world are *you* doing here?"

Mrs. Harris did not seem to appreciate this attention.

Carruthers read the papers, too.

"What do they want to bother them old stones for?" he asked himself. "They been here long as I can remember."

The question continued to pose itself. One morning he went so far as to tap the Cobblestones story in the newspaper with his finger and raise his eyebrows inquiringly.

Miss Augusta answered him. "They won't," she said.

Miss Louisa frowned. "Is all this conversation necessary?"

Carruthers went back downstairs. "That sure relieves my mind," he said to himself.

"The newspapers seem to be paying more attention to the de Gray sisters than to the cobblestones," Betty Linkhorn said.

"Well," her grandfather observed, "people *are* more important than cobblestones. Still," he went on, "*House of Mystery* seems to be pitching it a little stronger than is necessary. They just want to be left alone, that's all. And I rather incline to doubt that General M. M. de Gray won the Civil War all by himself, as these articles imply."

Betty, reading further, said, "*Hmmm*. Papa, except for that poor old Miss Tallman, there doesn't seem to be anyone alive—outside of their butler—who has ever *seen* them, even." She giggled. "Do you suppose that maybe they could be *dead?* For years and *years?*

And old Carruthers has them covered with wax and just dusts them every day with a feather mop?"

Mr. Linkhorn said he doubted it.

Comparisons with the Collier brothers were inevitable, and newsreel and television cameras were standing by in readiness for —well, no one knew just what. And the time for the repaving of Saratoga Street grew steadily nearer. An injunction was obtained; it expired. And then there seemed nothing more that could be done.

"It is claimed that removal would greatly upset and disturb the residents of Saratoga Street, many of whom are said to be elderly," observed the judge, denying an order of further stay; "but it is significant that the two oldest inhabitants, the daughters of General M. M. de Gray, the Hero of Chickasaw Bend, have expressed no objection whatsoever."

Betty wept. "Well, why *haven't* they?" she demanded. "Don't they realize that this is the beginning of the end for Saratoga Street? First the cobblestones, then the flagstone sidewalks, then the hitching posts and carriage blocks—then they'll tear up the common for a parking lot and knock down the three houses at the end to make it a through street. Can't you *ask* them—?"

Her grandfather spread his hands. "They never had a telephone," he said. "And to the best of my knowledge—although I've written—they haven't answered a letter for more than forty years. No, my dear, I'm afraid it's hopeless."

Said His Honor: "Nope, no change in plans. T'morra morning at 8 A.M. sharp, the cobblestones *go*. Awright, what's next?"

At eight that morning a light snow was falling. At eight that morning a crowd had gathered. Saratoga Street was only one block long. At its closed end it was only the width of three houses set in their little gardens; then it widened so as to embrace the small park—"common"—then narrowed again.

The newsreel and television cameras were at work, and several announcers described, into their microphones, the arrival of the

Department of Public Works trucks at the corner of Saratoga and Trenton Streets, loaded with workmen and air hammers and pickaxes, at exactly eight o'clock.

At exactly one minute after eight the front door of number 25 Saratoga Street, at the northwest corner, swung open. The interviewers and cameramen were, for a moment, intent on the rather embarrassed crew foreman, and did not at first observe the opening of the door. Then someone shouted, *"Look!"* And then everyone noticed.

First came Carruthers, very erect, carrying a number of items which were at first not identifiable. The crowd parted for him as if he had been Moses, and the crowd, the Red Sea. First he unrolled an old, but still noticeably red, carpet. Next he unfolded and set up two campstools. Then he waited.

Out the door came Miss Louisa de Gray, followed by Miss Augusta. They moved into the now absolutely silent crowd without a word; and without a word they seated themselves on the campstools—Miss Louisa facing south, Miss Augusta facing north.

Carruthers proceeded to unfurl two banners and stood—at parade rest, so to speak—with one in each hand. The snowy wind blew out their folds, revealing them to be a United States flag with 36 stars and the banner of the Army of the Tennessee.

And while at least fifty million people watched raptly at their television sets, Miss Louisa drew her father's saber from its scabbard and placed it across her knees; and Miss Augusta, taking up her father's musket, proceeded to load it with powder and ball and drove the charge down with a ramrod.

For a while the workmen debated what they ought do. Failing to have specific instructions suitable to the new situation, they built a fire in an ashcan, and stood around it, warming their hands.

The first telegram came from the Ladies of the G.A.R.; the second, from the United Daughters of the Confederacy. Both, curiously enough, without mutual consultation, threatened a protest march on the City Hall. In short and rapid succession followed indignant messages from the Senor Citizens' Congress, the Sons of Union Veterans, the American Legion, the B'nai Brith, the Ancient Order of Hibernians, the D.A.R., the N.A.A.C.P., the Society of the War of 1812, the V.F.W., the Ancient and Accepted Scottish Rite, and the Blue Star Mothers. After that it became difficult to keep track.

The snow drifted down upon them, but neither lady, nor Carruthers, moved a thirty-second of an inch.

At twenty-seven minutes after nine the Mayor's personal representative arrived on the scene—his ability to speak publicly without a script had long been regarded by the Mayor himself as something akin to sorcery.

"I have here," the personal representative declared loudly, holding up a paper, "a statement from His Honor announcing his intention to summon a special meeting of the Council for the sole purpose of turning Saratoga Street into a private street, title to be vested in the Saratoga Street Association. *Then*—" The crowd cheered, and the personal representative held up his hands for silence. "*Then,* in the event of anyone sustaining injuries because of cobblestones, the City won't be responsible."

There were scattered boos and hisses. The representative smiled broadly, expressed the Municipality's respect for Tradition, and urged the Misses de Gray to get back into their house, please, before they both caught cold.

Neither moved. The Mayor's personal representative had not reached his position of eminence for nothing. He turned to the D.P.W. crew. "Okay, boys—no work for you here. Back to the garage. In fact," he added, "take the day off!"

The crew cheered, the crowd cheered, the trucks rolled away. Miss Louisa sheathed her sword, Miss Augusta unloaded her musket by the simple expedient of firing it into the air, the Mayor's representative ducked (and was immortalized in that act by twenty cameras). The Misses de Gray then stood up. Reporters crowded in, and were ignored as if they had never been born.

Miss Louisa, carrying her sword like an admiral as the two sisters made their way back to the house, observed Betty and her grandfather in the throng. "Your features look familiar," she said. "Do they not, Augusta?"

"Indeed," said Miss Augusta. "I think he must be Willie Linkhorn's little boy—are you?" Mr. Linkhorn, who was seventy, nodded; for the moment he could think of nothing to say. "Then you had better come inside. The girl may come, too. Go home, good people," she said, pausing at the door and addressing the crowd, "and be sure to drink a quantity of hot rum and tea with nutmeg on it."

The door closed on ringing cheers from the populace.

"Carruthers, please mull us all some port," Miss Louisa directed. "I would have advised the same outside, but I am not sure the common people would *care* to drink port. Boy," she said, to the gray-haired Mr. Linkhorn, "would you care to know why we have broken a seclusion of sixty years and engaged in a public demonstration so foreign to our natures?"

He blinked. "Why . . . I suppose it was your attachment to the traditions of Saratoga Street, exemplified by the cobble—"

"Stuff!" said Miss Augusta. "We don't give a hoot for the traditions of Saratoga Street. And as for the cobblestones, those dreadful noisy things, I could wish them all at the bottom of the sea!"

"Then—"

The sisters waved to a faded photograph in a silver frame on the mantelpiece. It showed a young man with a curling mustache, clad in an old-fashioned uniform. "Horace White," they said, in unison.

"He courted us," the elder said. "He never would say which he preferred. I refused Rupert Roberts for him, I gave up Morey Stone. My sister sent Jimmy Taylor away, and William Snow as well. When Horace went off to the Spanish War he gave us that picture. He said he would make his choice when he returned. We waited."

Carruthers returned with the hot wine, and withdrew.

The younger sister took up the tale. "When he returned," she said, "we asked him whom his choice had fallen on. He smiled and said he'd changed his mind. He no longer wished to wed either of us, he said. The street had been prepared for cobblestone paving, the earth was still tolerably soft. We buried him there, ten paces from the gas lamp and fifteen from the water hydrant. And there he lies to this day, underneath those dreadful noisy cobblestones. I could forgive, perhaps, on my deathbed, his insult to myself—but his insult to my dear sister, that I can *never* forgive."

Miss Louisa echoed, "His insult to *me* I could perhaps forgive, on my deathbed, but his insult to my dear sister—that I could *never* forgive."

She poured four glasses of the steaming wine.

"Then—" said Mr. Linkhorn, "you mean—"

"I do. I pinioned him by the arms and my sister Louisa shot him through his black and faithless heart with Father's musket. Father was a heavy sleeper, and never heard a thing."

Betty swallowed. "Gol-*ly*."

"I trust no word of this will ever reach other ears. The embarrassment would be severe . . . A scoundrel, yes, was Horace White," said Miss Augusta, "but—and I confess it to you—I fear I love him still."

Miss Louisa said, "And I. And I."

They raised their glasses. "To Horace White!"

Mr. Linkhorn, much as he felt the need, barely touched his drink; but the ladies drained theirs to the stem, all three of them.

DOROTHY PARKER

A Pocketful of Parkers

One Perfect Rose

A single flow'r he sent me, since we met.
　All tenderly his messenger he chose;
Deep-hearted, pure, with scented dew still wet—
　One perfect rose.

I knew the language of the floweret;
　"My fragile leaves," it said, "his heart enclose."
Love long has taken for his amulet
　One perfect rose.

Why is it no one ever sent me yet
　One perfect limousine, do you suppose?
Ah no, it's always just my luck to get
　One perfect rose.

Social Note

Lady, lady, should you meet
One whose ways are all discreet,
One who murmurs that his wife
Is the lodestar of his life,
One who keeps assuring you
That he never was untrue,
Never loved another one . . .
Lady, lady, better run!

FIGHTING WORDS

Say my love is easy had,
  Say I'm bitten raw with pride,
Say I am too often sad—
  Still behold me at your side.

Say I'm neither brave nor young,
  Say I woo and coddle care,
Say the devil touched my tongue—
  Still you have my heart to wear.

But say my verses do not scan,
  And I get me another man!

FULFILLMENT

For this my mother wrapped me warm,
And called me home against the storm,
And coaxed my infant nights to quiet,
And gave me roughage in my diet,
And tucked me in my bed at eight,
And clipped my hair, and marked my weight,
And watched me as I sat and stood:
That I might grow to womanhood
To hear a whistle and drop my wits
And break my heart to clattering bits.

ROBERT EDMOND ALTER

She Fell Among Thieves

OUR SIX TRANS-JORDAN BOYS were spading back the hard, cindery earth crusted over a formation of flat, snug stones. Either they were uncovering an old, worthless, stone floor or they were uncovering an old, old, sunken, stone roof. Which might mean there was something under the roof. Something of archeological value.

I was sitting on a broken bit of wall just above them, supervising the job. Tanner, my partner, was in his tent with the shakes. He had been suffering from intermittent fever for the past few days. It was an old complaint with him. He'd had malaria in Cambodia. But that was before I knew him.

Twilight was flowing over the ironbound Jordan hills and the first fat drops of the long-awaited rain were just beginning to splat on the bone-dry dirt. They were widely separate at first, each silvery pear-shaped drop striking the earth like a tiny ripe fruit. I wished the boys would hurry—before the rain turned to buckshot.

The headman, Hassin, straightened up and grinned at me. He was very thrifty with his English words. If a grin would suffice, he always had one ready.

"Very good," I said.

They had uncovered the total area of the stone flooring or roofing. The stones formed a rectangle of, say, twenty by fifteen. I hunkered down for a closer inspection. The light was dimming rapidly.

It was a roof, all right, formed by overlapping courses of masonry crowned by hewn capstones. Couldn't be any doubt of it. So —was it possible that we had uncovered the first room of a lost city, or was it merely an old cellar? One way or another, the long-gone artisans who had laid this roof had put it together to last, to endure through centuries of dust-submerged oblivion.

Why? What was housed in the space under the old roof?

"Good," I said to Hassin. "Remove one of the cornerstones."

He translated the order and the Arabs went to work with crowbars, prying up one of the fair-sized slabs. A rectangle of black, hollow space appeared.

"Bring the ladder and the flashlight," I said.

Waiting for them, I fished out a stub of candle and lit it. A cold, black, unwholesome odor rose from the hole in the roof. I tested the air with the candle, to insure against poisonous gases. Then the boys sank the ladder in the opening and Hassin handed me the flashlight.

"You and the men stay up here," I said. "Understand? Give them cigarettes."

He grinned and nodded.

Tanner had taught me not to trust them. What they saw they talked about, and Tanner was the type of digger who preferred to keep his findings to himself—unless they were the usual run-of-the-mill artifacts. I started down the ladder.

The place itself was not truly clammy. It was the cold, dark air that gave the suggestion. I started to shiver. The pregnant raindrops followed me down the rungs.

I played the torch over the old stone walls, seeing here and there a faint white filigree of mold. The flooring was the earth itself and it was as black as sin.

The figure of a naked white female stood in the halo of light.

It took me so by surprise, that for an absurd moment, I almost blurted, "Excuse me." Then I had to laugh at myself. It was only a life-sized marble statue. It glowed, pale and cold and glorious, like moonlight. I went closer.

It was the most remarkable statue I had ever seen. The detail of the female was astounding. Her hair, eyelashes, fingernails, everything. She stood with her legs slightly apart, her torso turning at the hips, her head looking back over one shoulder.

It was the expression on her face that held me. It was enigmatic. Was it surprise, horror or ecstasy? At what strange sight was she staring? Involuntarily, I threw a mechanical glance over my own shoulder. Stupid!

Who had been the sculptor? How had the statue come here? How long ago? Excitement beat in my ears, slopped and slushed around in my brain like warm, heady wine. I was dead certain that I had made an exceedingly valuable discovery. I went up the ladder and dismissed the work crew. Hassin grinned at me as he turned away. Had he seen? Had he peeked through the roof?

I hurried through the rubble of our digging to Tanner's tent. The rain was coming down like wet bayonet points.

"You've never dreamed of a statue like this," I told Tanner. "She—she's beautiful! And that's a weak word. The look on her face. That enigmatic expression!"

Tanner grunted and threw a quinine pill into his mouth. He was a squat, powerful man. Bald. He was a freelancer. Had to be. There wasn't a reputable archeological group in the world that would touch him with a ten-foot pole. His methods were shady.

The Mexican Government was down on him for smuggling artifacts out of Yucatan; he had been run out of Cambodia for the same business, and the Greeks threw up their hands in horror at the mention of his name. I was new in the game and this was my first jaunt with Tanner. I didn't especially like the man, but I admired his professional knowledge. It seemed to me that I could

learn quite a bit about the financial end of archeology—the re-
wards—from a man like Tanner.

"I didn't think you could find statuary of this kind in this region," I said.

Tanner trembled with his fever and smiled wryly. "Neither did
I—not the way you describe her. But there could be a hundred
reasons how she came to this place. Let's have a look."

In raincoats, with topees on our heads, we went out into the
rain-lashed night. It was turning torrential. On our left, we heard
it machine-gunning the dark, salty surface of the Dead Sea.

Tanner took one look at the white statue and went into a
spasm of trembling. "G-god, she's f-fantastic, Miller! Ge-get the
Coleman lit."

I ignited the two meshy little bags and raised the lantern for
another look at the statue. Tanner prowled around her like an
Arab chieftain contemplating a marketable female slave.

"Fantastic! The exquisite d-detail of her!" He shivered violently,
hugging his upper arms. "She's old, old, old. My boy, you have no
idea how old. She's not Greek or Roman. Hell, even their greatest sculptors couldn't capture a facial expression like that. L-lord,
you can practically see the pores in her skin!"

Her face had me again—that enigmatic backward look. What
had she seen? I pulled my eyes away.

"Look at her coiffure," Tanner demanded. "The sculptor used
a Jewess for his model. Miller, I'll stake my reputation she dates
back to the Old Testament."

I wondered to which reputation he was making reference. Then
I found out. He turned to me and, in that sepulchral place,
with that pale, cold female standing by us, his fever-bright eyes
looked wild.

"Miller—do you have any idea what she's worth?" he asked, his
eyes greedy.

I shook my head, staring at him, not knowing what was coming.

"She's worth the thirty years I've spent grubbing in this business. Twelve times, I've tracked around the world searching for

her—without even realizing that she, or something as magnificent as she, existed! This"—he gestured toward the glowing female object—"is the treasure hunter's dream. This is the bonanza!"

I said, "You have more to say."

"Oh, yes. Oh, my God, yes! Much more. There's thousands in her, Miller. I know the right people. Two of them are in Paris. No questions asked. No mention of our names, ever. Nothing on paper. And no taxes. Right down the middle, boy. Fifty-fifty. If . . ."

"If I help you smuggle her out of the country," I said.

He laughed, his eyes leaping from my face to her face.

"There's no other way to work it. You know there isn't. That greasy governor of this district is as grabby as a fishnet strung with hooks. We're damned well lucky if he'll let us keep the worthless potsherds and beads we turn up. Do Hassin and the boys know about her?"

"I don't think so. I came down here by myself. But who ever knows about Hassin? He might have peeked when my back was turned."

Tanner nodded, shivering. "If he knows, he'll run right to the authorities. Not a doubt of it. Miller, we're getting her out of here tonight. Now."

I argued with him. Sure. For a minute, half-heartedly. But I was already caught by the infectious aura of his excitement. And we both knew it. I would be rich. Or, if Tanner failed to turn up the right buyer, I would at least be famous.

"You're certain of her age and value?" I'd accept any assurance.

"I know my business don't I? She's not listed in any catalog, I know. Her true worth will be any connoisseur's guess. But you can leave that part to me. All you have to do is help me get her out."

"To where? And how?"

He was sweating now.

"To Israel. That's the first move. I know someone influential there who'll help us for a little payola. Let's see. . . . We'd have to find and steal some kind of craft to cross the Dead Sea. And those damned Arab patrol boats would probably catch us halfway over. No. We'll take the truck and follow the shore down to Ein Hatseva. The barbed wire ends about fifteen miles below Sodom. All right?"

I nodded. "Right."

We had to rig up the block and tackle to get her out of the pit. She was heavy, but not as heavy as I thought marble would be.

"What do you think she is—chalcedony?" I asked as we hauled and shoved and strained in our own sweat, with the blinding torrent of rain pouring down on us. "You notice how she seems to have a certain sparkle about her in the light?"

"Could—could be just the moisture," Tanner grunted. "After eons of dampness down in that cellar."

Maybe. But the cellar had seemed as hermetically sealed as King Tut's tomb.

We swayed her up into the rain and the dark and Tanner said, "Get the truck. Hurry! For God's sake hurry!"

Our vehicle was an archaic old wreck, with tall, metal sides around the bed and an open top. I backed her up to the opening and trotted around to drop the tailgate. Tanner, holding onto the swaying statue in the tackle, watched me balefully. The gate came down with a rusty screech, like an ecstatic banshee busting loose. Cold, black water gurgled out of the bed. Tanner was shivering so violently that his teeth actually chattered.

"All right. G-get her b-by the sh-sh—*n-not by the head,* man! G-good God, be careful! B-by the shoulders!"

Grunting, heaving, shoving up, we jockeyed the gleaming woman-sized statue into the truck bed, Tanner hissing like a frantic boa constrictor. "Easy n-now! Careful! D-don't chip her!"

She was in, on her back with the rain peppering her body, her head slightly turned over her left shoulder, staring with that strange, fixed expression. At what? I slammed up the tailgate.

"I'll d-drive," Tanner said, and he gave me a shove.

Frowning with apprehension, I squelched around to the passenger side and climbed into the cab. Tanner slammed the door on his side, and for a long moment, he clung to the wheel with the shakes.

"My God, Tanner. You're in no shape for this. You'll kill—"

"Shut up! I've been through worse than this in Brazil and Cambodia. And for less—far less. W-what you want me to do? Crawl into my tent w-with my pills for a week? And let that damned governor snatch her away from me! I'll be all right, I tell you."

He turned her over and dumped her in gear and we jolted out of the mud with a tire spin and a neck-snapping leap and went lurching for the road.

"*Easy!*" I yelled.

"Shut up!" he snapped.

The old truck slid onto the road, careening slightly, found traction and went rolling into the gold-streaked blackness.

Outside, it rain, rain, rained. Inside, it dribbled, the moisture seeping around the door frames and the seams of the windshield. The truck skidded, swerved, slewed around, the tires treading for the ground, finding it, digging in and going forward again, and Tanner shivering and chattering and hunching down over the wheel.

And suddenly it all seemed crazy to me—this pellmell race into the night, down a muddy, nameless road, in a blinding rain, the fever-ridden, obsessed man clutching the swerving wheel at my side, and that pale, cold, wet female statue riding behind me, with her head turned over her shoulder and staring, staring. . . .

"Tanner," I said. "This is all wrong."

"Shut up! Damn it, Miller, shut up! Can't you realize what I've got in the back of this truck? It's my life. My entire life! Thirty years of searching and dreaming. Never honestly believing that she or anything like her would actually appear. And now she has. She has! And I've got her, and I'm going to get her out, and there's no power on earth can stop me!"

His heavy usage of the first-person possessive concerned me:

I've, I'm, me, my. . . . Did he still consider me his fifty-fifty partner? Was it the fever or the statue that was destroying his rationality?

A crystalline white eye materialized ahead of us, far down the road and coming on. It brodied around to a static, knifing stop and then a second, smaller light appeared and began to wigwag at us.

"That's a motorcycle," I said. "Someone signalling us with a flashlight to stop."

Then I realized that Tanner meant to drive right over the man and his cycle.

I slashed at his brake foot with my left boot. "You fool! You can't kill him!"

The truck went into a mad skid, the rear end skittering halfway around in a muddy pivot.

"Goddamn you!"

"Will you, for crapsake, take it easy!" I yelled at him.

A rain-coated Arab was picking his way toward us, slipping in the muck. He was one of the shore patrolmen and he carried an old World War II machine pistol in the cradle of his arm. He came up to Tanner's side and tapped the muzzle of the weapon against the streaming window. Tanner silently rolled it down.

"Your identification," the Arab said. "Where are you going?"

We dug out our wallets and showed him our ID cards. "Al Mazra," Tanner said in a quiet, almost dreamy, voice.

"You can see we're archeologists," I said. "We move from place to place, searching for Dead Sea scrolls."

"So?" the Arab said. "Let me see your permits, please."

"You have them," Tanner said. "They're in our wallets."

"Yes? And what are you carrying in this truck?"

"Only our equipment," I said.

"So? We will have a look."

Tanner reached down between his legs. The gesture had no meaning to me at that moment. I was in a panic to get out my door and meet the Arab at the back of the truck. I knew these people. They could be bribed.

The rain hit me like a break in a dike. I squelched to the back of the truck. The Arab came around the other end.

"Open up," he ordered.

The truck bed must have been like a bathtub. Rainwater was pouring out of every crack and hole. I put my hand on the right-hand bolt and smiled at him. "Look here . . ." I started to say.

Tanner's silhouette appeared behind the Arab and I saw his right arm swing up. The wrench literally bounced off the Arab's head and the machine pistol roared *ba-bap bap* straight in the air as the senseless man dropped into the mud.

"*Tanner!* You crazy idiot! We could have bribed him!"

Tanner said nothing. He threw the wrench aside and yanked the machine pistol free of the Arab. Then he said, "Drag him into the *karoo* shrub. Hurry!"

I stooped over the prostrate man, but in the night and the rain, I couldn't tell how badly he was hurt. He didn't seem right to me, though. Not at all.

"Tanner, he's badly hurt or dead."

The muzzle of the machine pistol tapped me coldly, jarringly, under the chin, then retreated. When I looked up, Tanner was aiming at my chest.

"Drag him into the bush."

"Tanner, listen to me. What if he's not dead? What if he's badly hurt? We can't leave him out here in—"

"Get him into the bush."

It wasn't necessary for him to say "or." I knew where I stood. Either I dragged the sad-apple Arab into the bush, *or* I joined him in the muddy road.

"You drive," Tanner said. And there were no ifs about that, either. Not with that gun aimed at my navel.

He herded me around through the passenger side and followed me into the cab. I released the brake and put her in gear and started to ease around the parked motorcycle. Tanner kept the gun at my right side.

"We could have bribed him, Tanner," I said again.

"No. He knew about us," Tanner insisted. "The governor sent him."

"Damn it, he *didn't* know about us! You hit him for no reason!"

"Shut up and drive!" The barrel nudged me in the ribs.

I was scared—sick-stomach scared. I could still hear the *bappity-bap* of that gun ringing in my ears. Those slugs would plow through me like darning needles through warm butter. I shut up and drove.

It poured rain. Tanner went in and out of the shakes. We passed through the district of Moab, then through sleeping Al Mazra. In less than an hour, we skirted Khinzirah and headed for As Safiyah. Another ten miles and we could cut west and aim for Beersheba, in Israel.

Tanner was starting to mutter to himself. ". . . so old she might go into the reckoning of millenniums. Tell you, she's of no known period. Might even belong to Abraham's time. Seems impossible, and yet . . . and yet . . ."

And yet, she lay back there in the bouncing truck bed, alone in the wet night, as we droned on through the pouring darkness.

It never let up, the rain, not for a moment. It seemed to cover the night land as Noah's deluge had once done.

Tanner figured we were past the barbed-wire barricades which separated Jordan and Israel, and he said, "Take the first turnoff west." He was burning up again. When I looked at him, he was swabbing sweat from his face with his left hand.

Maybe I could have slammed the brakes then and jumped him as he spun off balance. Maybe I could have gotten that gun away from him. But I didn't. I don't know why not. I didn't. I just drove on.

Tanner was wrong. The Arabs had extended the Jordan line.

The road we were on ran us smack into a frontier outpost. We were on top of it before I could do anything about it.

The white-and-red barricade was down, stabbing across our path, and an armed sentry was waving us to halt with his torch. There was a guardhouse, and an officer came through the door swathed to his eyes in a khaki-colored *cheche*.

I hit the brakes and we went into a mud-creaming skid. Tanner said one very old, very short Anglo-Saxon word and swung up the machine pistol. I grabbed at the barrel in a panic.

"Don't! There's a whole guardhouse of them. And look over there!" I pointed to the south of the sentry box.

Tanner hesitated, staring. Barbed-wire entanglements coiled off into the murk on either side of the road. A sandbagged sap squatted on top of the shallow bluff where the road curved down into No Man's Land. We could see a three-man crew hunkering around a light machine gun. The nest commanded the road.

"They'll cut us to shreds," I said.

Tanner sucked his breath as the armed Arab officer came squelching noisily through the mud.

Tanner relaxed with a soul-weary sigh. "I had it," he muttered. "I had the answer for at least one man's purpose of existence in this stupid damn world. And now . . ."

The officer, followed by the sentry who carried an old Lebel rifle, came up on my side and the sentry swung the barrel of the Lebel toward me significantly. I rolled down the window, still clinging tightly to the barrel of Tanner's gun with my right hand.

"Bism' Allah," I said to the officer, a lieutenant.

"Where do you think you're going?"

"We're American archeologists. We want to cross over to Beer-sheba."

"From where are you coming?"

"Upper Moab."

"Why didn't you cross at Sodom?"

Good question. I tried a bluff in assimilated anger.

"We're sick and tired of bribes. We thought if we came far enough south, we could cross over without having to pay tribute to every son of Allah who stood in our way with a gun at our heads."

The lieutenant laughed.

"You thought that, eh? What are you carrying into Israel?"

"Nothing."

He turned slightly without taking his eyes from me. "Keep your rifle at his head while I check the truck."

I stared blankly at the aimed Lebel rifle while my world turned slowly upside down. It wasn't just the trouble we would be in for trying to smuggle the statue out of the country; it might also be murder. Which would mean a firing squad.

I turned and looked at Tanner. He was trembling again and his eyes were side-slipping in his moist face, like a ferret caught in a trap. He still hadn't quite made up his mind.

"Don't," I whispered. "We'll never get through alive."

His sick eyes looked into mine.

"She's mine," he said hoarsely. "They can't take her away from me. I'd rather die than give her up!"

Then he snatched the barrel of the machine pistol from my hand.

The Arab lieutenant came slogging back.

"All right," he said. "You may pass." I stared. Then I said, "Thank you."

Tanner looked stunned. He gawked at the lieutenant. I put the truck in gear and let out the pedal and we shivered forward a few feet. Another sentry worked on some sort of gear in the dark and the white-and-red pole rose slowly into the raining sky.

I pressed the gas and we rumbled through the barricade and into the waiting blackness of No Man's Land. I didn't get it. I couldn't understand. True, I hadn't heard the tailgate drop, but surely the Arab officer had looked into the truck bed. Certainly he had climbed up on the rear bumper and investigated the back of the truck with his torch.

So why hadn't he seen the statue? Why hadn't he arrested us as smugglers?

"Stop the truck," Tanner said.

"What?"

"Stop! I want to look back here. Something's wrong."

"No," I said. "Not here. We're only a hundred yards from the Israel barricade. At this point, they can both see us."

"But something's wrong, Miller! What?"

"Wait! Damn it, can't you wait? The Jews are right ahead."

The armed Israelites came out from behind their barricade to meet us. I stopped the truck. This time it was a Jewish lieutenant who stepped up to the cab window.

"Who are you and what are you bringing into Israel?"

I don't know why I said it but I did. "Nothing. We're American archeologists."

"We'll see," the lieutenant said. "You realize that if you enter Israel now, you will not be permitted to re-enter Jordan?"

"That's all right by us," I said.

"We'll have to check the back of your truck," he said.

Tanner was already out his door. I shot out mine. The three of us met at the back of the truck.

The lieutenant looked at us with raised, wet eyebrows. "Something wrong?"

"That's what we want to find out," I told him.

Tanner and I unbolted the tailgate and let it drop with its usual screak. We stared into the rain-whipped truck bed. Water poured out of it like a miniature Niagara.

That's all there was—draining water. Nothing else.

"Stolen!" Tanner screamed. "My God, they stole her!"

"No!" I grabbed at his arm. "They didn't have a chance. We would have heard the tailgate. The Arab lieutenant was only back there for a few seconds by himself. He *couldn't* have gotten her out by himself. She weighs far too much."

"Then where?" Tanner wailed. "Where's she gone to? Oh, my God! *She's dissolved!* The rain! The filthy rain!"

He turned away from the open truck bed, away from me and the bewildered-looking lieutenant. And he started to laugh. The high mounting rocking laugh of insanity. He sat right down in the mud and roared with laughter until his breath failed him, and then he went into hiccupping, giggling sobs.

"Very nice," the lieutenant said to me. "Very nice what you've brought us. As if we didn't have our fair share already. All right. Let us get him into the infirmary. We'll have to strap him down."

The lieutenant and I left Tanner with a Jewish medic. We went outside and over to the barbed wire to have a smoke. The rain had petered to a sullen mist. I had nothing to say. I had only one question and it wasn't anything the lieutenant could answer.

Where had she gone? How? And when?

The medic came out and accepted a cigarette from the lieutenant.

"I gave him a shot to calm him down," he told us. Then he looked at me and jerked his thumb back at the infirmary shack. "Religious fanatic, eh?" he said.

"Who? Tanner? No. Why?"

"Because he keeps raving about Lot's wife," the medic said. "About how she looked back at the destruction of Sodom and Gomorrah even though God had warned her not to. And so she was turned to a pillar of salt."

JOSEPH WECHSBERG

The First Time
I Saw Paris

I SAW PARIS FOR THE FIRST TIME on a crisp, sunny morning in the autumn of 1926. I had gone there to study at the Sorbonne. My family was dissatisfied with the progress of my education in Vienna, where I had neglected to acquire an extensive knowledge in economics though I had become an expert at grand opera. They said that a semester or two at the Sorbonne would "round out" my education. They were worried because I had shown too much interest in music, writing, and other "breadless" arts.

"You must study law, finance, and economics," an old aunt said to me. "Think of the future of our bank!" The poor woman was bedridden with a chronic heart ailment, and her children didn't dare tell her that the family bank existed no longer.

I created a crisis when I declared, at my grandmother's seventieth birthday party, that I was going to play the violin—for money. The family was shocked. A nineteen-year-old boy doesn't know what he wants to do, they were saying; he is told by his uncles and aunts, who know best. My mother started to cry. Then Uncle Siegfried, my brother's and my legal guardian, came up with the idea of the Sorbonne.

"Let him go to Paris," he said. "A few months there will make him forget all that nonsense about playing the fiddle."

Uncle Siegfried owned a prosperous general store in Prívoz, a suburb of Ostrava on the banks of the Oder. The store was crammed with textiles, sauerkraut, stockings, pickles in large barrels, hardware, spices, open canvas bags filled with coffee, rice, barley, dried peas, dried lentils, fishing gear, smoked herring, meats, mousetraps, cheeses, sticks of sausages hanging from the walls, candles and holy pictures, chocolate, and flypaper. A wave of naphthalin, cinnamon, and bay leaf fused with the fragrance of toilet water and smoked herring, the smell of Pilsen beer, imported Jamaica rum, and the slivovitz that Uncle Siegfried and his clerks produced in the back room.

Uncle Siegfried was widely respected in the neighborhood for the quality of his slivovitz and for his generous credit policy. "If you wait long enough, you don't have to pay him back," his customers used to say. He was a powerful man with a large, black mustache and no hair on his head, which was always covered. In winter he wore a cap, in summer a Panama hat. Like the management of the State Railroads, Uncle Siegfried recognized only two seasons, winter and summer, irrespective of temperatures. Winter began on November 1, summer on May 1.

He ran his retailing empire from behind an old-fashioned cash register, where he received visitors, extended credit, handed candy to small boys, and made phone calls to the Odéon Cinema, which he ran as a profitable side line. Uncle Siegfried looked upon himself as a patron of the arts. Playing the fiddle was all right, he used to say—*after* working hours.

I arrived in Paris at the Gare de l'Est and told the taxi driver to take me to Montparnasse, on the Left Bank, where the Sorbonne and other institutions of higher learning are located, but he misunderstood my pronunciation of *Montparnasse* and took me to Montmartre instead. I knew nothing about Montmartre. I watched the meter click ahead with alarming speed, and when it jumped to nine francs I told the driver to stop, gave him ten francs, took my bag, and got out.

I found myself in the middle of a large square. The blue-white signs said PLACE PIGALLE. It seemed a nice, quiet neighborhood. I knew nothing of Paris, but to me, that autumn morning at half past eight, Place Pigalle looked like a typical Paris square.

Yes, I decided, this was the place to live. In a dark, narrow side street I found a small, dreary hotel, with broken windowpanes and a shield: RÉGENCE HÔTEL. The place appealed to me; it seemed run down and would probably be inexpensive. My funds were small and inelastic. Uncle Siegfried, mindful of the temptations that might beset a young man in Paris, had decided that I would be given a fixed amount of money for the entire trip. The length of my stay would depend on the strength of my moral principles. If I threw my money away on loose women and wine, I would be back soon. If I stretched my money, through thrift and asceticism, I could stay longer. Thus, Uncle Siegfried reasoned, Paris would teach me a lesson in morality and in the virtue of thrift.

The tiny, narrow entrance smelled of cheap perfume and of absinthe. There was no lobby. Behind a ramshackle desk sat a fat, middle-aged lady wearing a stained silk dressing gown that was bursting along the seams. So was the lady. She was reading a paper-bound novel and dunking a *croissant* into a glass of red wine. She didn't look at me when I came in.

I said I wanted a room. Without interrupting her reading she reached over her shoulder and took a key from one of the nails on the key-board behind her.

"*C'est pour un moment?*" she asked.

I said no, for a whole month.

She looked up, for the first time, and stared fixedly behind me as though she expected to see someone else.

"*Mais vous êtes seul!*" she said. Her mouth fell open, revealing a depressing job of French dentistry.

Her behavior was odd, but I'd read odd stories about the French. "Of course I'm alone," I said. "Now, how about the room?"

She lifted her fat forearms to heaven in a gesture of bewilderment, sighed deeply, took the key, and came out from behind the desk. The Régence Hôtel seemed to dispense with such luxuries as bellboys, receptionists, porters, elevators, telephones, palm trees, or room service. The *patronne* (I soon found out that she was the owner) ran the hotel herself with the help of François and Madeleine, a decrepit couple.

We walked up on the winding stairway. Halfway between two floors the *patronne* showed me the *cabinet,* which was built into the round wall, like a secret chamber. It was very quiet in the hotel, just what I wanted. I've always been a light sleeper. The *patronne* walked down a corridor and opened a room. On the floor was a heap of stockings, high-heeled shoes, dainty underthings, a dress, a hat, and the handbag of a lady who seemed to have shed her things on the spot, and in a hurry.

Then I saw the lady. She was in bed. Asleep. Her dark locks covered one side of her face, but the other was not unattractive. She wore no nightshirt.

The *patronne* gave an angry shrug, saying: *"Ça, alors!"* closed the door, and went on. The next room presented a Toulouse-Lautrec sort of still life of overturned bottles, filled ashtrays, half-filled glasses, and an empty, unmade bed.

"Excusez," the *patronne* said, to no one in particular, since the room was empty. She hastily closed the door and mumbled something. French people were certainly peculiar. The *patronne* didn't speak the academic French that I had learned in school. She would swallow the endings of most words. I decided that the French didn't speak good French.

The next room was unoccupied. It contained a washbasin behind a Japanese screen, a clothes hanger by the door, a light bulb dangling from a piece of string, and a very large bed. There was no closet. I asked how much the room was by the month. After much silent counting and lip-moving, the *patronne* quoted a price that was well within the limits of my budget. I was delighted. At the door she turned around and gave me what seemed to be a last glance of motherly affection.

"Listen, *mon petit,*" she said, "are you sure you really want to stay in here?"

I nodded. She gave a sigh. She said this room had no key, but that I could bolt it from the inside.

"I'm always downstairs," she said. "When I have my dinner, François will be at the desk."

She went out, shaking her head and muttering in despair. I thought she was a character straight out of Balzac. My acquaintance with Frenchwomen was based solely on the works of Flaubert and Balzac.

I was tired after sitting up all night on the train. I hung up my suit, washed—the water was ice cold—and went to bed. The bed was very comfortable.

When I woke up, it was dark outside. Every six seconds there was lightning, followed by no thunder. I got up and looked out. The lightning was caused by a neon sign across the street saying: LE PARADIS. From the street came the distorted sounds of voices, cars, whistles, shouts, and two hurdy-gurdies playing simultaneously *"Auprès de ma blonde"* and "Ain't She Sweet?" A drunk's voice shouted: *"Ta gueule!"*

Inside the hotel there seemed to be a lot of animation. People were laughing in the corridors, and I heard the clinking of glasses. Twice somebody tried to get into my room. I shaved—the water was piping hot now—dressed, and left the room. Downstairs two girls stood in front of the *patronne's* desk. The *patronne* was still reading her paper-bound book, which, I saw, was the memoirs of the Marquis de Sade.

"Bonsoir, chéri," said the older of the two girls. She had curls all over and wore a very tight skirt of a shiny material. She was spreading clouds of the cheap perfume that I'd smelled here in the morning. I said *bonsoir.*

"Qu'il est mignon!" said the other girl. She was from Bordeaux.

She must have been around when they discovered that 1899 would be an exceptional vintage in the Médoc.

"So you're the fellow who took the room for the whole month?" the curled girl said. Both exploded into coloratura laughter.

"Girls, *alors, alors!*" said the *patronne*.

"We're going to have fun with him," said Miss Vintage Bordeaux.

"Yes, *the whole month!*" the other one cried. That killed them. The curled one laughed so hard that she dropped her purse. I bent down and picked it up for her.

The door was opened and a girl and a man came in. The girl greeted everybody like an old friend, and the *patronne* said, "The twenty-three, Yvonne, as usual." The man behind her seemed embarrassed.

"That's *him!*" Miss Vintage Bordeaux said to the new girl, pointing at me.

"Oh!" she said, and gave me a respectful glance. Then she turned toward her escort and said: "Come on, *chéri,*" and they went upstairs.

I left the hotel. I knew the facts of life in Paris; I had been told by my worldly-wise friends that almost every Parisian hotel would let you have a room for a few hours, or a fraction thereof. In fact, a number of rooms on the lower floors were set aside for the pursuit of sinful happiness, I'd been told, but from the third floor up the guests were eminently respectable. My room was on the third floor.

At the corner I stood still and gasped. The blue-white signs still said PLACE PIGALLE, but the square didn't seem to be the one I had seen in the morning. It was past 10 P.M. All the shops were open and brightly lighted. On the sidewalk in front of the Café Le Paradis, an all-girl orchestra on a platform was playing "Singing in the Rain." In the middle of the Boulevard de Clichy several painters had put up their oils and watercolors under the trees. Near the Moulin Rouge a merry-go-round made shrieking noises. There was a cacophony of jazz music, organ grinders, automobiles tooting their horns, policemen using their whistles, sightseeing Cook's buses ("Paris by Night") using *their* horns, and passers-by using their lungs. It was worse than Times Square on New Year's Eve. Men in need of a shave edged up to me, speaking French and Arabic, offering "genuine Tabriz rugs," dirty postcards, Moroccan leather goods, their younger sisters, and a whitish powder that looked like, but wasn't, sugar. The peddlers hastily departed when two policemen approached. The police, I noticed, walked in pairs here.

I became aware of the persistent gnawing in my stomach. I hadn't eaten for over 24 hours. There was a restaurant next to Le Paradis, but the prices on the menu, which was displayed in a picture frame next to the entrance, ruled the place out for my budget. There were other restaurants, equally expensive. Most of them had dim lights. As you entered, the first thing you saw was a table with an arrangement of expensive fruit in a basket. The entrance was guarded by a couple of middleweights, wearing tuxedos. Once in a while a few dazed foreigners would stop to look at the fruit arrangement on the table, and before they could say *"crêpes Suzette,"* the middleweight tuxedos had bounced them in.

After a while I discovered a delicatessen that seemed to be a hangout of taxi drivers, night-club musicians, girls of small, if any, virtue, and artists from the nearby Cirque Médrano. I ordered a *bock*—a wineglass filled with beer—and a French sandwich, a paper-thin slice of ham between two large slices of French bread.

It was almost 2 A.M. when I got back to the Place Pigalle. The noise was worse than before. A second merry-go-round on the boulevard was doing good business. Below the window of my room a street trio—violin, accordion, and drums—was playing *"Mon Paris."* A thin, transparent-looking girl with big, haunting eyes and deep-red, heart-shaped lips sang the chorus in a shrill, somewhat guttural voice. After each chorus she would step among the listeners, who formed a circle around the band, to sell the sheet music of *"Mon Paris,"* for one franc a copy. Afterward the audience would join her and the orchestra in another chorus.

There was cheerful confusion in the narrow street, crowded with cops, drunks, girls, flower venders, tourists, more girls, peddlers, and *maqueraux*—"mackerels," as the French call their gigolos. In front of the Régence Hôtel, Miss Vintage Bordeaux stood with a silky-haired *maquereau*. He had polished fingernails and a tight-fitting jacket. She wanted to introduce me to him, but I escaped into the hotel and ran up the stairway. In my room I bolted the door from the inside.

I went to bed but I couldn't sleep. In the room next to me a man and a woman argued about the lousy sum of 20 francs. Downstairs the band was playing *"Les Fraises et les Framboises,"* and the girl's voice sang the chorus with a haunting ring. All night long doors were banged and people kept coming and going; glasses were broken and bells rang; once there seemed to be a fight among the girls in front of the hotel, and I heard police whistles. Dawn came reluctantly to the Place Pigalle, the neon sign LE PARADIS stopped blinking and I fell into exhausted sleep.

I woke up at noon, tired and miserable. I went down and told the *patronne* I couldn't sleep in her hotel and would have to leave. She understood my reasons but refused to refund my money. She talked darkly about laws and the *règlement,* and about two *brigadiers* who were her good friends.

As I didn't know then that in Paris a *brigadier* is not a general officer, but a cop on the beat, I dropped the subject of money. I was stuck. The next night I slept a little better and the following week I slept like a log. The trick was to stay up with the local populace and go to sleep with them at dawn. Once in a while everybody would be roused when the cops raided LE PARADIS and arrested the dope peddlers, but thereafter all would be quiet for a few days.

After a few weeks I became acquainted in the *quartier*. I found a *prix-fixe* restaurant in a quiet side street less than a hundred yards and more than a hundred years from Place Pigalle. The restaurant had a tiled floor, sprinkled with sawdust. There were small tables for four, covered with large sheets of white paper. When a guest had finished his meal, the waiter would write the *addition* on the paper, roll the paper with the bread crumbs together, and take it away. The next guest was given a fresh sheet of paper. The place was always crowded with little girls from the nearby department stores, pale clerks and minor officials from the *mairie* of the 18th Arrondissement whose faces had taken on the dusty, parchment-colored hue of their files.

There were no tourists with guidebooks, not even Frenchmen from the provinces. The guests of the restaurant never went to Place Pigalle after nightfall. One man lived right behind the Moulin Rouge music hall, but he had never been inside. They discussed Place Pigalle with clinical detachment, the way brokers discuss shares, and actors their makeup. "Pigalle," they agreed, was a *formidable affaire,* a sound business venture. If the silly foreigners wouldn't spend their money here, all the *Montmartrois* would have to pay higher taxes. "Pigalle," was all right as long as it created prosperity.

There was no fancy-fruit arrangement on a table inside the entrance of the Prix-Fixe, no tuxedoed middleweight waiting to bounce you in. The proprietor himself would stand there, and after you'd come to his place twice, he would shake hands with you, and you belonged. It was customary to shake hands with the waiter, too—but not with the guests at your table, no matter how well you knew them.

My waiter was Gaston, an old, asthmatic man who suffered from rheumatism. On days when the weather was about to change, he was ill-tempered and disinclined to listen to the guest's order. Instead he would bring the guest what he himself liked to eat. But his taste was excellent and usually he made a better choice than I should have done.

It was a nice place. I didn't know then that there existed restaurants in Paris like Lapérouse, L'Escargot, or La Tour d'Argent, where the *couvert* cost was as much as the entire menu here. I'm sure that my Prix-Fixe never made the Club des Cent or *Parmi les Meilleures Tables de France,* but at the age of nineteen the enthusiasm of the heart is stronger that the fastidiousness of the palate.

The omelet was light and fluffy, the *bœuf à la bourguignonne* delicious and aromatic, and the tender, small *bifteck* garnished with a heap of fresh watercress.

There were two menus, at 7.50 and at 10 francs, including the *couvert,* a small bottle of wine or a big bottle of *bière de Strasbourg,* and bread *à discrétion.* (Four pieces of bread were permissible, I learned; to take more was considered indiscreet.) The smaller menu offered hors-d'oeuvres, entrée, one vegetable, dessert or cheese. On holidays I threw my money away recklessly and feasted on the ten-franc menu, which included a fish course.

The menu was written in violet ink and was as difficult to read as a French railroad schedule. The specialties of the day, like deluxe trains, were marked in red ink. The specialties were "homely" dishes, *cassoulet toulousaine, haricot de mouton, blanquette de veau à l'ancienne,* or a *petite marmite.* Since Gaston liked those dishes, I had them frequently. Gaston said that the best thing one can say about a restaurant is that it's "almost like home." There were no *suprêmes d'écrevisses au champagne* on the menu, no *escalopes de foie gras à la Talleyrand,* or *crêpes Suzette.* But the *tripes* were marvelous.

I learned many things at the Prix-Fixe. You would place one end of the napkin inside your shirt collar. You would wipe your plate with a piece of bread until it was clean. Each course, even potatoes and vegetables, was served on a special plate, but you always used the same fork and knife. If you forgot and accidentally left your fork and knife on the used plate, Gaston would gently lift them up and place fork and knife on the paper sheet.

I often admired Gaston's virtuosity. He could carry three small wine bottles by their necks between forefinger and middle finger of his right hand, while his forearm was loaded with three plates; his left hand would swing a filled bread basket. When he wasn't carrying plates, he would cut long sticks of French bread into small pieces with the cutting machine. He always kept the baskets well filled.

Young couples would hold hands while they ate a delicious *raie au beurre noir* or a *vol-au-vent*. Between bites of food they would exchange passionate kisses. No one sitting near pretended to notice, but everybody looked pleased, and there was a glow of happiness about the place. Gaston beamed. He used to say that love enhanced digestion. Sometimes a girl who had exchanged kisses with a man one day would come with another man the next day and kiss him just as passionately. Infatuations were short-lived, but they were violent. It was a very romantic Prix-Fixe.

Most of the customers lived in the small, steep side streets off the Boulevard de Clichy, or up on the Butte Montmartre, the hill district north of Place Pigalle, which is crowned by Sacré-Cœur church and *les lieux où souffle l'esprit,* as Barrès once said. They had savings books with the nearest branch of the Crédit Lyonnais; their idea of a wild Saturday night spree was to go to a neighborhood cinema to see the latest exploits of Arsène Lupin, Master Detective, and afterward to sip a *chocolat* at Dupont (*"Chez Dupont Tout Est Bon"*). On Sunday afternoon they would venture out as far as the Grands Boulevards or the Champs Elysées to take a look at the shop windows and have a *bock* on a café terrace. The Champs Elysées, being actually located on the Right Bank, was considered neutral territory. Beyond, there was no man's land.

The inhabitants of the Butte Montmartre didn't recognize the rest of Paris, or of France. The Left Bank was like an unknown foreign country for which you needed visas and special permits. You had no business going there except on legitimate errands, such as to borrow money or to visit the grave of Baudelaire at Montparnasse Cemetery. The inhabitants of Montmartre were enthusiastic cemetery-goers. I spent many an afternoon at Montmartre Cemetery, visiting the graves of Heinrich Heine, Henri Murger, and Hector Berlioz. Several times in the course of my conversations at the Prix-Fixe I told my table companions that I had come to Paris to study at the Sorbonne. They thought I was joking and burst out laughing. I stopped talking about the Sorbonne and decided to round out my education, informally and alfresco, on the streets and squares of Montmartre.

The faculty had prominent experts in specialized fields of knowledge. My art instructors were the sidewalk painters. Some of them had been drinking-and-arguing companions of Utrillo, Utter, Suzanne Valadon, Friesz, and Raoul Dufy in the days when no one wanted their paintings. Now they were arguing *about* Utrillo and Dufy, and they would never agree. Often such arguments would last all night long. In the early dawn we would walk up to Montmartre Cemetery. At the grave of Mme Récamier we would stop and one member of the faculty, a leading anti-Utrilloist, would impersonate a grief-stricken Chateaubriand delivering the funeral sermon for Mme Récamier. He was a moving speaker, and at the end of his sermon everybody was crying. To refresh ourselves, we would proceed to the Moulin de la Galette for a couple of *bocks* before going to bed, between seven and eight in the morning.

My economics teachers were the sidewalk peddlers from North Africa. I learned a great many things from them that had never been taught at Vienna's College for World Trade. I learned which French department produced "genuine Tabriz" rugs (Bouches-du-Rhône), the difference between Moroccan art work in Fez and Meknès (Fez was best for copper work, Meknès for silver and leather), or how to make sure that profits from dope-peddling surpass occasional losses (choose a location guarded by older *brigadiers* who can't run as fast as you do).

I had become acquainted with the members of the trio who performed nightly in the street in front of the Régence Hôtel. Théophile, the drummer, was a scholarly-looking fellow with the face of a thoughtful airedale. His family lived in a respected neighborhood near the Porte d'Italie; his father, a patriotic, parochial, parsimonious *petit bourgeois,* was head bookkeeper at the Société Générale. In the daytime Théophile worked there as junior bookkeeper, but he said he wasn't interested in his daytime career. His

vocation was *le jazz,* hot or cold. He was in love with Claudia, the
transparent girl singer, and they were engaged to be married. It
was a shock for me, for I had become infatuated with the girl's
haunting voice.

Théophile's family didn't object to his nocturnal activities. He
said it would never occur to them to "travel"—*voyager,* he called
it—to Place Pigalle, 15 minutes by Métro from the Porte d'Italie.

"They might as well go to Papeete, Tahiti," he said, and
laughed. "But don't you have an uncle who doesn't like music?" I
asked him enviously.

He gave me a blank stare. He didn't know what I was talking
about.

Théophile's burning ambition was to become a regular *chef
d'orchestre* and run his own band. It would have five members, he
said. Around Pigalle, the *chef d'orchestre* is supposed to supply
the music, and Théophile had already built up a substantial reper-
tory of Salabert's Music Arrangements for Small Orchestra. He
owned three stands and the percussion instruments and drums on
which he performed. He promised to give me a *cachet*—a temporary job—as violinist as soon as he could set up his *affaire.*
A cousin of his mother owned a country inn with a garden and
dance hall in Saint-Rémy-les-Chevreuse, half an hour by train from
the Gare Montparnasse. The cousin, a patron of the arts, was will-
ing to give "Théophile et Son Orchestre" a start, provided it would
cost him nothing. Théophile figured out, with the help of two
itinerant math teachers from North Africa, that a dancing crowd
of 200, paying two francs a person, would enable him to pay each
of us 30 francs for the afternoon, and the cost of transportation
besides. The cousin would throw in supper gratis.

It sounded too good to be true, but one Sunday afternoon we
actually rode out on the train from the Gare Montparnasse. There
were five of us: Théophile and Claudia, a saxophone player, a
pianist, and myself. Everybody was uncomfortably silent as we entered Left Bank territory after crossing the Seine and proceeded
through enemy-infested boulevards to the railroad station. Théo-

phile carried the drums, and Claudia carried the music. She looked
lovelier, more haunting than ever.

"Théophile et Son Orchestre" were a great success at the
cousin's inn, but I wasn't. I'd been raised musically on Bach,
Brahms, and Beethoven, and now I had to dish out "Strawberries
and Raspberries" and *"Mon Paris."* My fox trots were too fast and
my jazz sounded like a Mozart minuet. I was glad when it was all
over and the orchestra was having supper in the big kitchen with
the cousin and his relatives: onion soup, thick slices of garlicky
gigot roti with *pommes lyonnaises,* salad, cheese, a good Beaujolais. It was a great day. Everybody had too much Beaujolais and
was singing. I had earned 30 francs and had been invited by a
French family, a rare distinction for a foreigner in France.

A few weeks later I ran into a former classmate from my home
town who had also come to Paris to round out his education at
the Sorbonne. He went there every day at eight in the morning,
and listened to many lectures: *"Le Consulat et l'Empire," "Les
Trésors de la Renaissance," "La Poésie en 1852," "Camées et
émaux."* He knew a lot about *"L'Histoire de la musique en
France,* but he had never heard of "Théophile et Son Orchestre"
and was shocked when I told him of Saint-Rémy-les-Chevreuse.
He had been to the Montparnasse Cemetery but had missed the
graves of Baudelaire and Maupassant. He knew no native Parisian.
He had been twice on the Eiffel Tower, and spoke an academic
and, to me, completely unintelligible French.

He took me to his favorite restaurant. The menu featured
goulash à la hongroise and *Wiener Schnitzel.* An anemic girl from
Scotland looked shocked when I wiped my plate clean with a piece
of bread. The proprietor was from Bucharest and shook hands
with no one. Afterward my classmate took me to the Rotonde and
showed me the American expatriates. The evening was a total loss.
At 10 P.M. I sneaked away on the Nord-Sud subway. I was lonely
and homesick for Montmartre.

It was good to get back to Pigalle. The racket of the hurdy-
gurdies, whistles, shouting people, and tooting horns was like the

ticking of an old grandfather clock in a quiet living room. I was back where I belonged. I didn't tell my friends where I had spent the evening. I was ashamed.

I might have stayed in Montmartre indefinitely if Uncle Siegfried hadn't come to Paris one night on the late train. He had gone on business to Switzerland, to buy Lindt chocolates and Emmental cheese, and had promised my mother to look me up. He went straight to the Régence Hôtel. When I came there at two in the morning, as was my habit, I found my uncle sitting at a sidewalk table next to the all-girl orchestra of the Café Les Paradis. I noticed that Uncle Siegfried, ordinarily a strong man—he had been decorated with the Austrian Army's gold *Tapferkeitsmedaille* for bravery in the First World War—looked pale and shaken.

I sat down next to him on the terrace. That, it turned out, was a mistake. Several of my North African economics teachers came by and tried to sell my uncle genuine Tabriz rugs from the Bouches-du-Rhône department, and one, Mohammed ben Ali, sat down beside us, offered my uncle his young sister and the white stuff that looked like, but wasn't, sugar, and told me that he'd just won a 300-meter race against an aging *brigadier*.

Then Théophile and Claudia dropped in. Claudia kissed me on the cheek and Théophile paid me 30 francs for last Sunday's work. My uncle wanted to know what the money was for. I told him proudly about my job with "Théophile et Son Orchestre." My uncle said nothing, but his face took on the hue of moldy herring. Miss Vintage Bordeaux ambled by, stopping at our table, giving me a kiss on the cheek, and asking: *Ça va, chéri?"* She winked at my uncle and said there was nothing she would deny a friend of a friend of mine, and then she gave *him* an affectionate kiss on the cheek and pulled up a chair.

Uncle Siegfried shouted: *"Garçon!"* paid, and made a humiliating scene on the café terrace, in front of my friends and teachers. He shouted that I was a rotter, giving a bad name to my family, and that he was going to take me to the Left Bank, *right now!* My friends and teachers listened in horrified silence.

That very night Uncle Siegfried moved me out of the Régence Hôtel and installed me in a drab, dull *pension* near the Sorbonne. It belonged to a former *lycée* teacher from Grenoble, who had coffee for breakfast and read the collected works of La Rochefoucauld. Visitors had to be announced at the desk. There was a bed check at midnight. The roomers were dull, rich boys from Switzerland and Indo-China who pretended to be gifted and broke. They would get up at seven-thirty in the morning, and spend all day long at the Sorbonne.

I was miserable in Montparnasse. In the evening I would sneak off for a few hours to Place Pigalle. But it wasn't the same any more. My friends and teachers began to suspect me of being a Left Bank spy. Miss Vintage Bordeaux no longer kissed my cheek. Théophile hired another violinist, and one night Mohammed ben Ali offered me his white stuff, as though I were a tourist. I was no longer welcome in Montmartre and stopped going there. A few weeks later I left Paris and went back home.

LORD DUNSANY

The Speech

"CRIME," SAID THE OLD JOURNALIST one night at his club. "One reads a good deal about violence nowadays; but I never read of a crime that would make a story like the one that there was when I was young. *That* would have made a story. But it was all hushed up."

"No doubt for some good reason," a younger journalist said.

"Yes," said the old journalist. "It had to be. They were extremely careful not to disturb the peace of Europe in those days. That, you see, was what the crime was about. There was a young man, scarcely remembered now, brilliant though he was—the Honorable Peter Minch. His old father you would never have heard of. A totally obscure old peer, Lord Inchingthwaite. But people heard of Peter Minch in his time. He was an M.P. and the coming man of the Opposition, one of those coming men that you never hear any more of.

"At the time that I tell about, he was going to make a speech in the House. Things had been simmering for some time. What this young fellow was going to say just at that time wasn't going to help the peace of Europe at all. What he was going to say would have prodded Austria pretty hard; and, if Germany had supported

131

her in what would have been quite justifiable resentment, Russia would not have liked it, and the fat would have been in the fire. But there was no stopping Minch. He was a bit of a firebrand. The government couldn't stop him, of course. And as for the Opposition, he was their fancy man, and they were probably thinking more of how it would embarrass the government than annoy the Austrians."

And then (the old journalist went on) the extraordinary thing happened. A man walked into the central office of Minch's party, without giving his name, and said quite clearly that he had sure information that was not exactly a message, and must not be taken as a threat but only a warning, that that speech would never be made.

"What do you mean?" said the Chairman of the Party.

"I mean," said the man, "that there is an organization with which I have nothing to do, nothing whatever, who are determined to stop that speech, and who are powerful enough to do what they threaten. It is not I that threaten. I came to warn you."

"Do you mean," said the Chairman, "that they are going to use force?"

"They will use whatever is necessary," said the stranger. "We— that is, *they*—consider war to be the greater evil."

"War?" said the Chairman. "Who says we are making war?"

"Their information," said the stranger, "is that what Mr. Minch is going to say just at this time will bring war nearer. They are well informed, and they have told me they are convinced that causing the death of one man is preferable to the risk of disturbing the peace of Europe."

Well, as politely as possible, the Chairman told him to go to hell. And as the man left, he said, "That speech will not be delivered. Under no circumstances will it be, in the House."

The Opposition told Scotland Yard. And *they* took the matter up at once, and assured the Chairman of the Party that the entire police force of the metropolis would be available. Police protection on an enormous scale was given to Minch at once.

I think Scotland Yard must have known more than they ever

told about the organization that was making that threat, because they said at once that the man that had called on the Chairman of the Party would have been a man named Hosken. And that's who he turned out to be. The Chairman asked them then if they would arrest him. But the chief inspector said: Better not—better leave him at large, and he might give them more information. And he did.

The Chairman of the Party was sitting in his office with a burden removed from his mind, for he felt that the police had everything well in hand, when in walked this extraordinary man again. They let him come in, because they wanted to hear what the fellow had to say. They addressed him by his name this time, and I think it gave the Chairman a little childish pleasure to imply by doing so that they knew all about him.

"Well, Mr. Hosken," said the Chairman, "is there anything more that you wished to tell us?"

A faint smile from Hosken greeted the use of his name. And then he said, "Only to say that all those policemen will not enable Mr. Minch to make that speech and start a debate in Parliament, while things are as they are just now abroad."

"If Mr. Minch desires to speak in the House, as he has every right to do, he will certainly do so," said the Chairman.

"I have come to say," said Hosken, "that if he will put it off, so as to give things time to simmer down, the powerful organization with which a friend of mine is in touch will take no action."

"If you mean by 'things' the state of affairs in Europe, we are not concerned with them. No one in Europe can deny us free speech," said the Chairman.

"It would be an open defiance," said Hosken, "and would lead to war."

"You must understand," the Chairman said to Hosken, "that we cannot tolerate any more blackmail."

"Certainly, sir," said Hosken. "Only there will be no speech in Parliament by Mr. Minch for at least a week. And, if you stop him peacefully, there will be no need for violence."

Then he smiled and walked out.

Well, that's how things were (went on the old journalist)—tension rather acute, and this fiery young man going to start a debate in the House that would put all the fat in the fire, and perhaps set it overflowing and scalding all Europe, and a powerful organization of blackmailers—for they were nothing less—determined that that debate should never take place, and that one man's murder was nothing compared to war. And against the blackmailing gang was practically the whole of the police force of the metropolis. I needn't go into the precautions taken by the police. They took them all. Minch was constantly under observation by at least two of them. I doubt if anyone was ever more watched in London.

They soon ran Hosken down, but did not arrest him. All they did was to keep him under observation. I fancy they thought that he would be more useful to them that way.

On a Wednesday morning everything was all ready. Minch was going to speak at seven that evening. His whole family were going to be there, his old father in the Peers' Gallery, and all the rest of his family in the Ladies' Gallery. The police had a cab for Minch which was entirely bulletproof, even to windows of plate glass that was over an inch thick.

Well, the precautions were more than would have been taken for moving bullion from the Bank of England. They asked Minch to be at the House by three o'clock.

As he and his police escort arrived, a messenger boy handed a note to the inspector in charge of the guard. He opened it and saw an anonymous note, saying: *Mr. Minch will not make that speech today*. He smiled, because once inside the precincts of the Houses of Parliament murder was quite impossible.

Minch's family were to arrive at half past six. At three o'clock, a dull debate opened. And yet the tension was electric, for everyone present knew the threat of the gang. The dignity of Parliament was at stake, and most of the members, even on the side to which Minch was going to cause so much trouble, put that first. Slowly the tension heightened, as the clock moved round to four.

And in that heightened tension everyone seemed to know what

everyone else was thinking. They knew when any speaker was intending to be funny, and all laughed quickly and nervously, even before the little joke came.

And then, at five minutes past four, a note for Mr. Minch was handed by a policeman to the inspector, who passed it to the sergeant-at-arms, who went into the chamber and gave it to Minch. Minch opened it and turned white.

"My father is dead," he said to a member beside him. "He's been murdered."

"I am terribly sorry," said the other man. "What happened?"

Minch handed the note to him. His father had been shot dead in his house. The murderer had escaped.

"And your speech," said the other member. "I am afraid—"

"No," said Minch. "That can't stop me. Nobody could be sorrier than I am. But private grief is one thing, public duty another."

"But, look here," said the other member. "I mean—you're a peer."

"I'm a what!" said Minch.

"You're a peer now," said the other again.

"My God!" Minch answered.

Well, that was the end of that. The gang had done it. They attacked as any man of sense would always attack, at the weakest point, where nobody was expecting it. And nobody did think of poor old Lord Inchingthwaite. He was quite obscure. But the moment he died, Peter Minch became a peer, and could make no more speeches of any sort in the House of Commons.

And he couldn't even make his speech in the House of Lords, until he had taken his seat, and all that took time. He did make the speech at a meeting that week in what had been his constituency, but Austria took no notice of that.

"So war was averted," said the young journalist.

"Well, yes," said the old journalist. "Not that it made any difference in the end."

EDMUND G. LOVE

Railroad Fever

WHEN I WAS IN THE THIRD GRADE, our teacher asked the twelve boys in my class what we were going to do when we grew up. Nine of the twelve said they were going to be locomotive engineers. The other boys may or may not have meant what they said, but I did. I loved the railroad and everything on it with a passion that has seldom been equaled.

I went to the West Side school. Flushing had two schools, one on each end of town, but the new school building (built in 1878) had room for only the kindergarten and ten of the twelve grades. The other two grades went across the river to the West Side school and from the time I entered the first grade, at the age of five, my grade was one of the two that were relegated to that place of exile.

The West Side school was the original school in Flushing township. It had been built before the Civil War. It was a one-story building of red brick and had two rooms. The larger of these rooms had two blocks of seats separated by a big open space in the center. The teachers' desks occupied this open space, one facing in each direction. The smaller of the two rooms, at the back of the building, was a recitation room. One grade would march in there while the other studied, then come back into the big room while the other grade went out to do its reciting.

The West Side school was a primitive building. It had no running water and no sanitary facilities. Electric lights and a furnace to replace the old potbellied stove had been added only a year before I started going there. Drinking water came from an ancient pump in the front yard. If a student wanted a drink of water he raised his hand with one finger extended. When recognized he would go out and hold one hand over the spigot while pumping with the other. When his hand was holding back enough water for his needs, he would bend over and drink from his cupped hand. If a student had to go to the bathroom, he held up two fingers and skittered out the back door. Two outhouses were perched on the very back of the school property and getting to them involved a walk—or a run—of half a block. Going to these outhouses in the wintertime involved some physical courage.

The best thing about the West Side school, as far as I was concerned, was the fact that it was located close to the railroad. The outhouses sat on a bluff that overhung the tracks at the very point where they made their turn southwest to Durand. From most of the windows of the school I could look up the tracks toward Durand for a mile or more. I could hear the northbound trains whistle for the crossing three miles away. I couldn't hear the southbound trains until they whistled for Henry Chatters's crossing just north of town, but that was still five minutes away. Even if I had been content to just sit and watch the trains out the windows, I couldn't have picked a better place to go to school. But I wasn't content to do just that.

The West Side school was just a half mile south of the depot. I could run out the back door of the school, duck down the bluff behind the two outhouses, and be right on the tracks. From there I could run along the ties to the depot in less than five minutes. (It took me a little longer the other way because it was uphill.) School started at nine o'clock in the morning. It let out at quarter of twelve for dinner. It reconvened at 1:15 for the afternoon session, and dismissed for the day at four o'clock. This fitted exactly with the way the trains ran. The southbound morning passenger train was due at the depot at quarter of nine, just fifteen minutes before school began. The northbound morning passenger train was due at 11:56, just eleven minutes after we were dismissed for the noon recess.

In Flushing the depot was a good half mile from the post office in the middle of town so Charlie Thompson, a round little retired farmer, had been hired to carry the mail back and forth to the depot. Every morning at exactly 8:30 he would carry the mailbags out of the post office and put them in his buggy. Once the mail was loaded into the buggy, he would unhitch his horse, climb into the seat, and start off at a slow trot across the old iron bridge and up the west Main Street hill. He would arrive at the depot, hitch his horse to a post around at the back, load the mail on the baggage wagon, then wheel it out beside the tracks.

My life was coordinated with Charlie Thompson's journey to the depot. It was my custom to rush out the front door of our house in the morning, dash across the street, and climb the wire fence around J. B. French's farm equipment yard. I would streak down the alley that ran through the yard, let myself in the back door of Mr. French's hardware store, race down the aisles and out the front door into Main Street. I would arrive at the post office and climb into Charlie Thompson's buggy just as he clucked to his horse. I never missed this connection, although I suppose Charlie *did* wait for me a few times. When we got to the depot I would help Charlie drag the mailbags out of the buggy and load them on the baggage wagon. Then, while he was wheeling it out to the tracks, I would duck into the waiting room, shinny up the wall, and reach around through the ticket window and release the lock on the door into the station agent's office. Once inside there I would rush over to the telegrapher's desk and look through the train passage book to see what engines had gone through town during the night. When anyone had forgotten to put down an engine number, as they sometimes did on the midnight Flyer, I reprimanded him. This didn't happen often after my first year of going to the depot, I can tell you.

By the time I had finished checking the operation of the railroad, John Reardon would be rumbling across the Main Street crossing. I would go out and talk to him while he oiled his engine. He seemed to like me because I never failed to inquire after the health of number 2248. He would crawl back up into the cab and sit down. In a moment Beans McAuslin, his fireman, would get the signal from Mr. Blades, the conductor, and reach up and pull the bell rope. John Reardon would pull on his throttle and number 2248 would chug slowly up the hill toward Durand. I would run along the tracks after it as fast as I could go, scramble up the bluff behind the school, and usually settle into my seat just as the last bell stopped ringing. On a snowy day when the drifts were deep I was often slowed down, but I managed to keep from being marked tardy by stopping in the outhouse and taking off my mackinaw. The teacher always assumed that I had been to school on time and had taken a little detour.

During the morning session of school, the only train to come to Flushing was the northbound local freight. This usually waited for John Reardon in Lennon, the next town to the south, and then came on north. I knew number 2315 almost as well as Burt Emans, the engineer, did, so I never felt it necessary to check closely on this train. I preferred to save my emergency procedures for the afternoon. However, if number 2315 had been turned into the shop for repairs and there was a substitute engine, I felt justified in taking the necessary steps. I could tell a strange engine as far away as I could hear it. The minute Burt Emans blew the whistle on one of these strangers for Morrish's crossing, three miles away, I had my hand in the air with two fingers up. When the teacher noticed me and nodded, I would let myself out the back door and run for the outhouse. Instead of entering it, however, I would duck around behind it and slide down the bank to the railroad tracks. I would usually arrive there just as Burt Emans came panting up to the switch at the south end of town.

While the brakeman was unhitching the engine from the train, I would be talking up to Burt in the cab, finding out all I could about the new engine. When he moved on into town to start switching, I would scramble back up the bank and return to school.

When we were dismissed at quarter of twelve, I was out the back door and running. I usually made it to the depot just as the northbound passenger train came around the bend at the south of town. I would check with John Reardon to find out how number 2248 had survived the thirty-mile round trip to Durand, talk a little to Mr. O'Brien, the railway mail clerk, and then, as the train chugged up the north grade out of town, I would help Charlie Thompson load the mailbags into his buggy. Upon arrival at the post office I would help drag the mail in and wait until Frank Perkins, the postmaster, opened the first-class bag. If there was a special delivery letter in it, and there usually was one, Frank would get down the clipboard with the delivery sheet, hand the letter and the board to me, and I would go off at a run to deliver it. I got eight cents for delivering each special delivery letter and I think I delivered every one that came to Flushing from the time I was six years old. I made as much as ninety-six cents in some weeks and that was a lot of money for a boy my age. Most of the time I considered myself independently wealthy. I've since come to believe that I may have been the youngest employee the United States Post Office Department ever had.

By the time I'd delivered the mail and got home for the noon-time meal, the rest of the family was just sitting down. Although we all sat around the dining-room table for dinner, as we called it, there was no real formality about it and there were no penalties for being late. I would rush through the food put before me and run most of the way back to school, stopping off in the post office to drop the delivery sheet and collect my eight cents. The afternoon was always busier for me than the forenoon because there was a steady stream of trains. By that time the local freight would have finished most of its switching at the towns along the CS&M

and the main line would be clear so that the chief dispatcher could release a flood of through trains. The northbound afternoon mani-fest—a fast freight with cars for Saginaw only—arrived first. The two engines unhitched for their trip to the water tank in full view of the West Side school. This train was usually pulled by number 2300 and number 2258. I knew both of those engines well and I never bothered to do anything more than look out the window at them. (The second engine of a doubleheader never whistled, so I had to look to make sure that a stranger didn't slip by. Even if there was a new engine, I didn't do any more than look because I knew it would be back in town on the southbound manifest late in the afternoon.)

The afternoon extras were the trains that played hob with my schooling. Sometimes two or three of them would go by in the course of an afternoon and they were always pulled by engines that I knew little about. The minute I heard a whistle my hand would go up and I would duck for the back door. The funny thing about all these visits to the outhouse was the fact that my teachers never seemed to realize exactly what was going on. For five of the seven years I attended the West Side school one of the two teachers was my aunt Esther and she finally got so worried about my frequent trips to the outhouse that she told my mother my kidneys ought to be checked. My mother put me in the family car and drove me over to Flint to see Dr. McKenna, our family physician. When I got into the room alone with the doctor and he started asking me questions, I had to tell him the truth. He sat down in his chair and laughed. Still laughing, he rolled up the top on his desk and wrote a note for me to take to my teacher. It said simply that I should be allowed to drink as much water as I wanted to and that I should be allowed to go to the bathroom as often as I wanted to, until further notice. This was an unexpected boon to me because it turned out that I could go and watch trains on either one or two fingers. Dr. McKenna died in 1960 at the age of ninety-six, and for all the rest of his long life he never failed to inquire gravely about my kidneys.

The minute school was over in the afternoon, I headed straight for the depot again. I usually got there about the time the southbound way train pulled in to take water. (The way train went north early in the morning and concerned itself only with seasonal chores. It hauled livestock on Monday, sugar beets in the fall, and sand and gravel in the summer.) The way train was followed closely by the southbound afternoon manifest, and finally by the southbound local freight.

Of all the trains on the line, my favorite one was that local freight. Although it switched around Flushing for two hours each morning, I rarely saw it close up during the week until it arrived on its return trip to Durand in the afternoon. Burt Emans usually brought his whole train right on down to the water tank at that time because he pulled only a few empty cars southbound. While Burt was oiling number 2315 and the fireman was taking water, I crawled up into the cab for the ride out to the south end of town. When the brief business of afternoon switching was done and number 2315 pulled up the hill toward Durand, my railroading was usually concluded for the day. I rarely hung around the depot until the evening passenger train came south. It arrived too close to suppertime, besides which fact I already knew that it would be pulled by number 2248 and that it would be right on time. Occasionally, when John Reardon took a day off and I heard a strange whistle, I would rush over and meet the train. Of course, by the time the trains began rushing through town in the late evening—there were a great many of them after the evening passenger train went north—I was already in bed. All I could do was lie there and listen to the whistles and wonder what I was missing.

Saturdays and other days when there was no school were always my happiest times. I was at the depot bright and early. The minute Burt Emans brought number 2315 into town and parked the less-than-carload freight car at the freight depot I climbed up in the cab and took my seat on the fireman's box. When the brakemen signaled that they were ready to start the day's switching I reached up and pulled the bell rope, then leaned out the window

on my elbows like all enginemen did. As time passed I learned
everything about an engine. I could read the various gauges. I
knew what each valve wheel was for, and I knew the difference
between the train brake and the engine brake. I stoked the firebox
and I helped take water. I blew the whistle. I could couple and un-
couple the cars on the train and I was taught how to bleed an air
line. I knew all the hand signals. I talked the language that the
trainmen used. I called a caboose a way car, the semaphore a red
board. I knew what a brakeman meant when he set out a car or
lined up a switch. I referred to the different kinds of engines as
the railroad men did, as goats, jacks, uprights, stokers, Panamas,
or pigs, not as 4-4-0's or 2-8-2's. I did errands for all the trainmen.
I took Burt Emans's jug over to the hotel and had it filled with
coffee. I bought sandwiches for Pete Ronald, one of the brakemen,
and cigars for Mac Durfee, the other brakeman. I even helped Mr.
O'Brien, the railway mail clerk, identify names when he couldn't
make out the handwriting on the envelopes.

My complete absorption with the CS&M railroad had numerous
benefits. There was the matter of prestige. I was never the best
baseball player or football player in the village, but I always managed to get chosen first on all the teams because I controlled certain privileges. No other boy could get a ride in the cab of number
2315 without my approval and once they crawled up the iron steps
of the engine they were under my complete control. When I took
a boy to Burt Emans to get him a ride, Burt would consider the
matter thoughtfully and then nod. "All right. You do just what
George tells you." (All the railroad men called me George, for
what reason I do not know unless it was because they called all
small boys George.) Under such a blanket endorsement I could
naturally let one of my friends ring the bell at the proper time or
even throw a shovelful of coal into the firebox occasionally.

My life on the railroad had drawbacks, too. I am always surprised that I ever got an education at all. I was not content just to
sneak out the back door of the West Side school. I spent a lot of
my time in school drawing pictures when I should have been do-

ing arithmetic or practicing penmanship. I think I must have
drawn a picture of every engine that showed up in Flushing. All
of them, from 2242 to 2321, were supposed to be the same, but I
saw differences in them. When I drew number 2254, I made it
swaybacked. That's the way it looked to me. The front springs on
number 2283 were weak so that it looked like a hound dog sniffing
along the rails. I drew it that way.

I suppose all this had some influence on my later life. Whether
it came from my preoccupation with engine numbers or not, I
have always had a phenomenal memory for numbers of all kinds.
I can remember telephone numbers, license numbers, street numbers, and statistics. I never get on a bus, subway car, or train without automatically noticing the number of the car. But there is
more to it than that. When I look back at my early life I find myself inclined to relate everything to the railroad.

RAY BRADBURY

The Foghorn

OUT THERE IN THE COLD WATER, far from land, we waited every night for the coming of the fog, and it came, and we oiled the brass machinery and lit the fog light up in the stone tower. Feeling like two birds in the gray sky, McDunn and I sent the light touching out, red, then white, then red again, to eye the lonely ships. And if they did not see our light, then there was always our Voice, the great deep cry of our Fog Horn shuddering through the rags of mist to startle the gulls away like decks of scattered cards and make the waves turn high and foam.

"It's a lonely life, but you're used to it now, aren't you?" asked McDunn.

"Yes," I said. "You're a good talker, thank the Lord."

"Well, it's your turn on land tomorrow," he said, smiling, "to dance the ladies and drink gin."

"What do you think McDunn, when I leave you out here alone?"

"On the mysteries of the sea." McDunn lit his pipe. It was a quarter past seven of a cold November evening, the heat on, the light switching its tail in two hundred directions, the Fog Horn bumbling in the high throat of the tower. There wasn't a town for a hundred miles down the coast, just a road, which came lonely through dead country to the sea, with few cars on it, a stretch of two miles of cold water out to our rock, and rare few ships.

"The mysteries of the sea," said McDunn thoughtfully. "You know, the ocean's the biggest damned snowflake ever? It rolls and swells a thousand shapes and colors, no two alike. Strange. One night, years ago, I was here alone, when all of the fish of the sea surfaced out there. Something made them swim in and lie in the bay, sort of trembling and staring up at the tower light going red, white, red, white across them so I could see their funny eyes. I turned cold. They were like a big peacock's tail, moving out there until midnight. Then, without so much as a sound, they slipped away, the million of them was gone. I kind of think maybe, in some sort of way, they came all those miles to worship. Strange. But think how the tower must look to them, standing seventy feet above the water, the God-light flashing out from it, and the tower declaring itself with a monster voice. They never came back, those fish, but don't you think for a while they thought they were in the Presence?"

I shivered. I looked out at the long gray lawn of the sea stretching away into nothing and nowhere.

"Oh, the sea's full." McDunn puffed his pipe nervously, blinking. He had been nervous all day and hadn't said why. "For all our engines and so-called submarines, it'll be ten thousand centuries before we set foot on the real bottom of the sunken lands, in the fairy kingdoms there, and know *real* terror. Think of it, it's still the year 300,000 Before Christ down under there. While we've paraded around with trumpets, lopping off each other's countries and heads, they have been living beneath the sea twelve miles deep and cold in a time as old as the beard of a comet."

"Yes, it's an old world."

"Come on. I got something special I been saving up to tell you."

We ascended the eighty steps, talking and taking our time. At the top, McDunn switched off the room lights so there'd be no reflection in the plate glass. The great eye of the light was humming, turning easily in its oiled socket. The Fog Horn was blowing steadily, once every fifteen seconds.

"Sounds like an animal, don't it?" McDunn nodded to himself. "A big lonely animal crying in the night. Sitting here on the edge of ten billion years calling out to the Deeps, I'm here, I'm here, I'm here. And the Deeps do answer, yes, they do. You been here now for three months, Johnny, so I better prepare you. About this time of year," he said, studying the murk and fog, "something comes to visit the lighthouse."

"The swarms of fish like you said?"

"No, this is something else. I've put off telling you because you might think I'm daft. But tonight's the latest I can put it off, for if my calendar's marked right from last year, tonight's the night it comes. I won't go into detail, you'll have to see it yourself. Just sit down there. If you want, tomorrow you can pack your duffel and take the motorboat in to land and get your car parked there at the dinghy pier on the cape and drive on back to some little inland town and keep your lights burning nights. I won't question or blame you. It's happened three years now, and this is the only time anyone's been here with me to verify it. You wait and watch."

Half an hour passed with only a few whispers between us. When we grew tired waiting, McDunn began describing some of his ideas to me. He had some theories about the Fog Horn itself.

"One day many years ago a man walked along and stood in the sound of the ocean on a cold sunless shore and said, 'We need a voice to call across the water, to warn ships; I'll make one. I'll make a voice like all of time and all of the fog that ever was; I'll make a voice that is like an empty bed beside you all night long, and like an empty house when you open the door, and like trees in autumn with no leaves. A sound like the birds flying south, crying, and a sound like November wind and the sea on the hard, cold shore. I'll make a sound that's so alone that no one can miss it, that whoever hears it will weep in their souls, and hearths will seem warmer, and being inside will seem better to all who hear it in the distant towns. I'll make me a sound and an apparatus and they'll call it a Fog Horn and whoever hears it will know the sadness of eternity and the briefness of life.' "

The Fog Horn blew.

"I made up that story," said McDunn quietly, "to try to explain why this thing keeps coming back to the lighthouse every year. The Fog Horn calls it, I think, and it comes. . . ."

"But—" I said.

"Sssst!" said McDunn. "There!" He nodded out to the Deeps.

Something was swimming toward the lighthouse tower.

It was a cold night, as I have said; the high tower was cold, the light coming and going, and the Fog Horn calling and calling through the raveling mist. You couldn't see far and you couldn't see plain, but there was the deep sea moving on its way about the night earth, flat and quiet, the color of gray mud, and here were the two of us alone in the high tower, and there, far out at first, was a ripple, followed by a wave, a rising, a bubble, a bit of froth. And then, from the surface of the cold sea came a head, a large head, dark-colored, with immense eyes, and then a neck. And then —not a body—but more neck and more! The head rose a full forty feet above the water on a slender and beautiful dark neck. Only then did the body, like a little island of black coral and shells and crayfish, drip up from the subterranean. There was a flicker of tail. In all, from head to tip of tail, I estimated the monster at ninety or a hundred feet.

I don't know what I said. I said something.

"Steady, boy, steady," whispered McDunn.

"It's impossible!" I said.

"No, Johnny, *we're* impossible. *It's* like it always was ten million years ago. *It* hasn't changed. It's *us* and the land that've changed, become impossible. *Us!*"

It swam slowly and with a great dark majesty out in the icy waters, far away. The fog came and went about it, momentarily erasing its shape. One of the monster eyes caught and held and flashed back our immense light, red, white, red, white, like a disk held high and sending a message in primeval code. It was as silent as the fog through which it swam.

"It's a dinosaur of some sort!" I crouched down, holding to the stair rail.

"Yes, one of the tribe."

"But they died out!"

"No, only hid away in the Deeps. Deep, deep down in the deepest Deeps. Isn't *that* a word now, Johnny, a real word, it says so much: the Deeps. There's all the coldness and darkness and deepness in the world in a word like that."

"What'll we do?"

"Do? We got our job, we can't leave. Besides, we're safer here than in any boat trying to get to land. That thing's as big as a destroyer and almost as swift."

"But here, why does it come *here?*"

The next moment I had my answer.

The Fog Horn blew.

And the monster answered.

A cry came across a million years of water and mist. A cry so anguished and alone that it shuddered in my head and my body. The monster cried out at the tower. The Fog Horn blew. The monster roared again. The Fog Horn blew. The monster opened its great toothed mouth and the sound that came from it was the sound of the Fog Horn itself. Lonely and vast and far away. The sound of isolation, a viewless sea, a cold night, apartness. That was the sound.

"Now," whispered McDunn, "do you know why it comes here?"

I nodded.

"All year long, Johnny, that poor monster there lying far out, a thousand miles at sea, and twenty miles deep maybe, biding its time, perhaps it's a million years old, this one creature. Think of it, waiting a million years; could *you* wait that long? Maybe it's the last of its kind. I sort of think that's true. Anyway, here come men on land and build this lighthouse, five years ago. And set up their Fog Horn and sound it and sound it out toward the place where you bury yourself in sleep and sea memories of a world where there were thousands like yourself, but now you're alone, all alone in a world not made for you, a world where you have to hide.

"But the sound of the Fog Horn comes and goes, comes and goes, and you stir from the muddy bottom of the Deeps, and your eyes open like the lenses of two-foot cameras and you move, slow, slow, for you have the ocean sea on your shoulders, heavy. But that Fog Horn comes through a thousand miles of water, faint and familiar, and the furnace in your belly stokes up, and you begin to rise, slow, slow. You feed yourself on great slakes of cod and minnow, on rivers of jellyfish, and you rise slow through the autumn months, through September when the fogs started, through October with more fog and the horn still calling you on, and then, late in November, after pressurizing yourself day by day, a few feet higher every hour, you are near the surface and still alive. You've got to go slow; if you surfaced all at once you'd explode. So it takes you all of three months to surface, and then a number of days to swim through the cold waters to the lighthouse. And there you are, out there, in the night, Johnny, the biggest damn monster in creation. And here's the lighthouse calling to you, with a long neck like your neck sticking way up out of the water, and a body like your body, and, most important of all, a voice like your voice. Do you understand now, Johnny, do you understand?"

The Fog Horn blew.

The monster answered.

I saw it all, I knew it all—the million years of waiting alone, for someone to come back who never came back. The million years of isolation at the bottom of the sea, the insanity of time there, while the skies cleared of reptile-birds, the swamps dried on the continental lands, the sloths and saber-tooths had their day and sank in tar pits, and men ran like white ants upon the hills.

The Fog Horn blew.

"Last year," said McDunn, "that creature swam round and round, round and round, all night. Not coming too near, puzzled, I'd say. Afraid, maybe. And a bit angry after coming all this way. But the next day, unexpectedly, the fog lifted, the sun came out fresh, the sky was as blue as a painting. And the monster swam off away from the heat and the silence and didn't come back. I suppose it's been brooding on it for a year now, thinking it over from every which way."

The monster was only a hundred yards off now, it and the Fog Horn crying at each other. As the lights hit them, the monster's eyes were fire and ice, fire and ice.

"That's life for you," said McDunn. "Someone always waiting for someone who never comes home. Always someone loving some thing more than that thing loves them. And after a while you want to destroy whatever that thing is, so it can't hurt you no more."

The monster was rushing at the lighthouse.

The Fog Horn blew.

"Let's see what happens," said McDunn.

He switched the Fog Horn off.

The ensuing minute of silence was so intense that we could hear our hearts pounding in the glassed area of the tower, could hear the slow greased turn of the light.

The monster stopped and froze. Its great lantern eyes blinked. Its mouth gaped. It gave a sort of rumble, like a volcano. It twitched its head this way and that, as if to seek the sounds now dwindled off into the fog. It peered at the lighthouse. It rumbled again. Then its eyes caught fire. It reared up, threshed the water, and rushed at the tower, its eyes filled with angry torment.

"McDunn!" I cried. "Switch on the horn!"

McDunn fumbled with the switch. But even as he flicked it on, the monster was rearing up. I had a glimpse of its gigantic paws, fishskin glittering in webs between the finger-like projections, clawing at the tower. The huge eye on the right side of its anguished head glittered before me like a caldron into which I might drop, screaming. The tower shook. The Fog Horn cried; the monster cried. It seized the tower and gnashed at the glass, which shattered in upon us.

McDunn seized my arm. "Downstairs!"

The tower rocked, trembled, and started to give. The Fog Horn and the monster roared. We stumbled and half fell down the stairs. "Quick!"

We reached the bottom as the tower buckled down toward us. We ducked under the stairs into the small stone cellar. There were a thousand concussions as the rocks rained down; the Fog Horn stopped abruptly. The monster crashed upon the tower. The tower fell. We knelt together, McDunn and I, holding tight, while our world exploded.

Then it was over, and there was nothing but darkness and the wash of the sea on the raw stones.

That and the other sound.

"Listen," said McDunn quietly. "Listen."

We waited a moment. And then I began to hear it. First a great vacuumed sucking of air, and then the lament, the bewilderment, the loneliness of the great monster, folded over and upon us, above us, so that the sickening reek of its body filled the air, a stone's thickness away from our cellar. The monster gasped and cried. The tower was gone. The light was gone. The thing that had called to it across a million years was gone. And the monster was opening its mouth and sending out great sounds. The sounds of a Fog Horn, again and again. And ships far at sea, not finding the light, not seeing anything, but passing and hearing late that night, must've thought: There it is, the lonely sound, the Lonesome Bay horn. All's well. We've rounded the cape.

And so it went for the rest of that night.

The sun was hot and yellow the next afternoon when the rescuers came out to dig us from our stoned-under cellar.

"It fell apart, is all," said Mr. McDunn gravely. "We had a few bad knocks from the waves and it just crumbled." He pinched my arm.

There was nothing to see. The ocean was calm, the sky blue. The only thing was a great algaic stink from the green matter that covered the fallen tower stones and the shore rocks. Flies buzzed about. The ocean washed empty on the shore.

The next year they built a new lighthouse, but by that time I had a job in the little town and a wife and a good small warm house that glowed yellow on autumn nights, the doors locked, the chimney puffing smoke. As for McDunn, he was master of the new lighthouse, built to his own specifications, out of steel-reinforced concrete. "Just in case," he said.

The new lighthouse was ready in November. I drove down alone one evening late and parked my car and looked across the gray waters and listened to the new horn sounding, once, twice, three, four times a minute far out there, by itself.

The monster?

It never came back.

"It's gone away," said McDunn. "It's gone back to the Deeps. It's learned you can't love anything too much in this world. It's gone into the deepest Deeps to wait another million years. Ah, the poor thing! Waiting out there, and waiting out there, while man comes and goes on this pitiful little planet. Waiting and waiting."

I sat in my car, listening. I couldn't see the lighthouse or the light standing out in Lonesome Bay. I could only hear the Horn, the Horn, the Horn. It sounded like the monster calling.

I sat there wishing there was something I could say.

RUSSELL BAKER

A Brace of Bakers

1. After Success, What?

WHEN SUCCESS ARRIVES it is followed two weeks later by a secretary. The secretary sits at a desk outside the door looking efficient, forbidding, and protective.

Almost at once, she turns success into a problem. It would look bad to let her just sit there buffing her nails. She must be given work to do so that everyone can see that success is no bed of roses. It must also be impressed upon her that she is working for a man who counts for something.

American business culture has evolved several ways for dealing with these problems. One way is to give the secretary plenty of dictation. The standard practice is to call her in and dictate a dozen letters to important men whose names will awe her.

For example: "Dear Walter, You have rung the bell again with this morning's column, which I read aloud to my wife over breakfast. I was reminded of something Richelieu once said when confronted with a similar situation during the . . ."

Or: "Take a letter to John Steinbeck. 'Dear John, Just a note to tell you that I have been rereading *Tortilla Flat* with the kids and . . .' " Walter and John may resent a total stranger's addressing them by their first names but, being gentlemen, they are unlikely to reply snappishly. Moreover, the letters will make work for their secretaries and, thus, lighten the drain on their own creative energies.

Once a success has impressed his secretary with his importance, she will be on guard against common nuisances who want to waste her employer's valuable time. The problem here is to persuade some common nuisances to come to the office so the secretary can throw them out. Encyclopedia salesmen are very useful for this purpose.

The problem about making an appointment for someone to come in so he can be turned away is that the secretary will insist on making the telephone call. A success who makes his own telephone calls rarely makes it all the way to the board room.

In fact, one of the first duties of success is to waste other people's time by making them hang on a dead telephone receiver. Everyone knows how this works. The phone rings. A feminine voice says, "Mr. Sterling?" "This is Sterling speaking." "Will you hold on, please, for Mr. Success?" The line goes dead while Sterling holds on.

Nine chances out of ten, Sterling has never heard of Mr. Success, but he is curious to find out who he is. It is unthinkable for a man with a secretary to call Sterling directly. For one thing, Sterling himself may have a secretary, in which case she will humiliate him by saying that her man is in conference. Secretaries have little respect for men who make their own phone calls.

The common practice is to have the secretary place four or five calls, asking each party to hold on, and then go to the water cooler for a chat with the office boy. This lets all the people holding dead receivers understand where they stand in the cosmic order.

It is not clear why success must have everyone wait on it at the telephone. If a successful man were going to call personally on someone, he would not send his secretary ahead to ask his host to drop everything and sit tight for the arrival of Mr. Success. If he did, the host would tell her to take a flying leap at the switchboard.

Some people, of course, have no phone manners at all. When asked, "Will you hold on, please, for Mr. Success?" They say, "No," and hang up. Fortunately for the man with a secretary to keep busy, these are a small minority.

It is apparent from all this why so few successes ever go on to do great things in life. The job of making work for their secretaries takes everything out of them before they move up to their first oil painting on the office wall.

2. The American Discovery of Europe

How MANY SCHOOL CHILDREN being driven to distraction about that tiresome old sailor, Columbus, realize that Europe was discovered by Americans before America was discovered by Columbus?

In the year 1490 a flotilla of six giant canoes bearing 533 Arawak Indians from the Bahama Islands made a landfall on the coast of Spain after a relatively smooth paddle of 63 days on the North Atlantic.

They had set out to find a water route to California, which their great captain, Aberquakkicola, was convinced could be reached by sailing east. Aberquakkicola was no fool. Unlike Columbus, who spent years floundering around the Caribbean under the impression that he was somewhere near China, Aberquakkicola immediately realized that this new landfall was not California.

"In this land," he wrote in his log, "there are neither redwood trees, nor smog, nor Oh-Boy-Burger Stands among the people. We have discovered a new world." With his entire crew, he waded ashore, stuck a tobacco plant in the earth in the traditional Arawak method for staking land claims, and took possession of his new world in the name of Chief Aberquidnunc.

The handful of Spanish peasants who witnessed the ceremony were naturally disturbed. They sent word of the landing to the neighborhood duke, who put on his armor and rode down to see what was going on. Aberquakkicola greeted him gently.

"Be thankful, old man who wears metal skin," he said, "for your country has been discovered by representatives of the great bronze father, Aberquidnunc."

"You're talking absolute rot," said the duke. "You can't discover my country. It's been here for thousands of years."

"There is much sense in what you say," said Aberquakkicola. "We must return to the canoes and discuss this." And he withdrew with all his men. That night they held a great council around the captain's paddle.

A few among them, but not many, for the Arawak were a peaceful people, favored chopping up the old man in the metal skin, enslaving the able-bodied adults and colonizing the place.

Aberquakkicola shamed the men who proposed this. "It is only natural that these savages resent being discovered," he reasoned, "for in their ignorance they cannot be aware that they have been living here undiscovered by our entire civilized world for thousands of years. Would we not resent it if some one of these savages in his metal skin landed in our country and insisted that he had discovered us?"

The men saw the good sense of this reasoning and agreed that they should return to the Bahamas and leave the savages in peace.

Many of Aberquakkicola's men, however, had come with gold, which they hoped to trade among the natives for glass beads and trinkets, and they pleaded for permission to spend one last day trading on the shore. Aberquakkicola, seeing no real maliciousness in gulling the savages of a few beads and trinkets, approved.

Meanwhile, the duke had summoned his fellow dukes to the castle for a midnight council and repeated the story of having been "discovered."

"It's impertinence," said one particularly testy duke. "It's intolerable impertinence for a flotilla of naked wanderers without so much as a pike or an arquebus to wade out of the Atlantic and discover Europe. What's more, they're probably dangerous. They're probably lying out there in those canoes right now plotting how to do the same thing we'd be plotting to do if the shoe were on the other foot and we had discovered them."

The council agreed that it would be dangerous to let a large mass of utter strangers get away with discovering Europe. And so, when the Arawak came ashore next day to trade, the armies of the dukes fell upon them and killed them in droves.

Aberquakkicola and a few of his men escaped in a single canoe and drifted for several years. When he returned finally to the Bahamas he was too late to teach his fellow tribesmen the wise lesson he had so bitterly learned in Europe about how one civilization should treat its discoverers from another. The Arawak had already been discovered by Columbus, whose forces were established in depth.

Which, of course, explains why those silly science-fiction movies are perfectly right when they wheel up the U.S. Army to deal with the flying saucer in Little Jimmy's back yard.

FERENC MOLNÁR

The Best Policy

MONSIEUR BAYOUT, PRESIDENT OF THE NATIONAL FARMERS BANK, sent for his secretary Philibert.

"Tell me, Philibert," he said, "who is this man Floriot down at our Perpignan branch?"

"Floriot? . . . That's the cashier. He's acting as manager temporarily. You remember, sir, the old manager, Boucher, died, and we haven't found anyone to put in his place yet. Floriot's looking after things meanwhile. There isn't very much business in Perpignan."

Monsieur Bayout took a letter from his desk. "Well, apparently he's robbing us. I've had this letter from Perpignan. It's anonymous, I admit, but . . ."

He handed Philibert a not very clean sheet of notepaper on which, in a somewhat unformed hand, the following lines were written:

To the President of the National Farmers Bank.
Dear Sir,
  We farmers are putting our hard-earned savings in your bank at

Perpignan, and one fine day we shall wake up and find it has gone bankrupt and all our savings are lost. It is bound to happen the way things are going on here. You probably don't know that the cashier, Monsieur Floriot, has been embezzling money for months past. He must have put away a tidy packet by now, but of course by the time you high and mighty gentlemen in Paris realize what's going on, all the money will be gone.

"Send an inspector down to Perpignan tomorrow, Philibert," the president said. "But tell him to be tactful, we don't want to upset the man. There's probably no foundation for the story."

Monsieur Floriot, temporary manager of the Perpignan branch, stared at the inspector from Paris with horrified amazement. "Inspect my books?" he echoed. "What, now? In the middle of the month? Without any notification? It's a bit unusual, isn't it?"

The inspector felt sorry for the agitated little man. "There's nothing to worry about, Monsieur Floriot. We do this at all our branches from time to time. The president gets these sudden fits. It's only a formality. I'll be through in half an hour."

"Yes, but people will talk, especially in a small place like this," Floriot wailed. "Everyone will be saying that I've been up to something shady. Think of the disgrace!"

"Nobody's going to know anything about it," the inspector said, a trifle impatiently. "That is, of course, unless you yourself talk. Well, can I see the books now?"

Two days later Philibert entered the president's room. "I'm able to report on the inspector's visit to Perpignan, sir. Everything in the books is in order. Not a single sou missing."

"Good. One really ought not to pay any attention to these disgusting anonymous-letter writers. Thanks, Philibert."

Less than a month later, the president again summoned his secretary. "It's quite ridiculous," he said testily. "But I've had another anonymous letter about Perpignan. The writer declares that the books weren't properly examined. Apparently Floriot made such a song and dance about the whole thing that an accomplice had time to replace the stolen money. We really ought to have gone into the matter more thoroughly."

"Do we have to make another investigation?" Philibert asked ruefully.

The president drummed his fingers on the desk. "I don't like doing it. All the same, it's a duty we owe to our clients. If there is something in it, and people find out afterwards that we were warned, there'll be a nasty scandal. I'm afraid the only thing to do is send the inspector down again. And this time let him do the job thoroughly. I want to clear this up once and for all."

The same day three of the bank's most reliable inspectors set out for Perpignan. This time Monsieur Floriot was really taken by surprise. One of the officials kept guard over him, while the other two carried out a thorough examination of his accounts, lasting over four hours. They found nothing missing, and the books in perfect order.

"I only wish things were as satisfactory in all our branches," the chief inspector said, as he bade farewell to the completely shattered Floriot.

A week later: "Monsieur Floriot of Perpignan is waiting to see you, sir," Philibert announced.

Departing from his usual habit, Monsieur Bayout rose and advanced towards his visitor with an outstretched hand.

Floriot, however, gave a stiff little bow. "I've come to hand in my resignation, sir," he said.

"Your resignation? You can't mean that, my dear Floriot. Why?"

"You found it necessary to have my books examined twice running, sir. Naturally it caused a lot of talk. Even though I was proved to be an honest man, it made a bad impression. People are saying there must have been some good reason why the head office sent down twice to have my affairs investigated. My reputation's gone. I'm not a young man, and I have a wife to think of."

Monsieur Bayout was deeply moved. "I'll make it my personal responsibility to see that your name is cleared. Wait a minute, though. . . . The manager's job is still vacant, would you like to have it? No one could doubt your honesty then, could they? Yes, and you'll get a substantial increase in salary, too."

"You really mean . . ." Floriot stammered.

"Of course, of course, my dear fellow. The bank will be fortunate in keeping the services of so conscientious a worker."

Back at his home in Perpignan, Pierre Floriot slid his feet into the comfortable felt slippers his wife handed him.

"At last!" he grunted, in a good-humored voice. "What's the use of being an honest man if nobody hears of it? I might have gone on being a cashier for years and years, and the people at the head office would never have known how honest I was."

"They know now!" Madame Floriot beamed, regarding her husband with admiration. "Those letters were a wonderful idea of yours!"

JULIUS FAST

Grow Old Along With Me

ACTUALLY, IT ALL STARTED WITH AN OFFHAND REMARK, a remark I never really meant. I was young, hardly eighteen, and always spoiling for a fight—verbal or physical. It didn't matter if I was usually wrong. The fun of the argument was what I was after. I was big, raw-boned and good looking, and my mind was as alert as my body.

That year Charlie Watson and I had both been trying to beat each other out with pretty Peggy Talbert. Peg had spent an hour one pleasant spring afternoon playing one of us against the other, and then she had flounced out of the ice cream parlor with two girl friends, her long ruffled skirt giving us the most tantalizing glimpse of a pair of pretty ankles.

Charlie leaned his chair back on two legs and pushed his straw boater up on his head, then he arranged the crease in his narrow trousers. It's funny that way back at the turn of the century they were wearing trousers just as tight as they are now.

"That woman is almost as bad as the devil," he muttered. "She'll lead a man right to hell."

I admired the knowledgeable way he delivered the line, but I didn't give an inch. "Oh, I don't know."

He looked at me in amusement. "What don't you know, Ko-vacs?"

I had to come up with something good, preferably a little shocking. "I don't know why you assume the devil is all bad."

He lifted one eyebrow, a trick I knew he'd spent days practicing, and I went on casually. "For sheer malice the devil can't hold a candle to a girl like Peggy. In fact," I had found my road and I began to elaborate, "all in all, the devil is much maligned. Every literary reference to the man makes him out a perfect gentleman, yet always gotten the best of. The Faust story—sure, the doctor had it coming to him, but who got the raw deal? Old Satan. No. Charlie, I say that the devil is a good man and I for one will stick up for him."

"Well, you do that!" Charlie laughed and stood up. "Kovacs, you're a crazy galoot. Where you get your ideas . . ." but there was admiration in his voice and I smirked in self-satisfaction.

I was heading home a bit later when a pleasant-faced stranger in a formal black suit and high hat fell into step beside me. "I want to thank you, Mr. Kovacs."

I was startled. "You're welcome, but I'm afraid I don't . . . that is . . ." I hated to admit that I didn't know him. That was pretty embarrassing when he knew my name.

He didn't give me much help, just grinned a bit shyly, but a nice grin.

"You have the advantage of me," I added with what I hoped was adult dignity.

His grin grew wider. "But I won't take it. Surely you recognize me."

The nice easy way he spoke put me at my ease. All at once it didn't seem so bad, not knowing who he was, because in a way I did know him. It was on the tip of my tongue.

"You stood up for me today and very nicely too."

"I stood up for you?"

"Yes, of course." He lifted his hat and I saw two pink horns poking out of his curly black hair. "Satan, Eddie. I really should have calling cards. It would make this much easier. Take a deep breath."

You know, I was so stunned I could hardly do anything but obey. I filled my lungs and instantly began to cough.

"Sulphur and brimstone," Satan said with a little-boy expression of delight. "Cleans the nasal passages, doesn't it?"

I straightened up and said, "Look, a joke is a joke, but—"

He didn't answer but he stopped smiling and stared at me and his eyes—there was something about his eyes—they were black, a deep, deep black, the kind of black that had no end to it—and maybe no beginning. I knew right then for sure and my legs just buckled under me. We were on a broad, tree-lined street, the houses set far back with wide lawns and porches, and I could see girls with long white dresses rocking in wicker rockers while laughter, thin and sweet, floated under the trees. Such an ordinary street!

I sat down on the curb and he sat beside me. "Put your head down, boy, between your legs and push up." He placed his hand on my head and I pushed against it, feeling the blood rush back to my face. "There. That will do it. Are you all right, Eddie?"

I licked my dry lips. "You really are Satan!"

"That's as silly as saying you really are Eddie Kovacs. Of course I'm Satan. Now here's my proposition . . ."

I put out my hand and touched his chest. "No. Now look, I may have stood up for you, but that was kind of like, well . . ."

"Oh come, don't spoil it all, you certainly did stand up for me."

"But I'm not making any deal. My soul is inviolate." I felt a little pompous, but awfully righteous.

He winced. "Dear, dear boy. I don't want your soul . . ." He paused and sighed. "There you are. Even you who stood up for me today, even you are a victim of the worst kind of predetermined judgement. Innocent until proven guilty. Now that's a laugh."

"I'm sorry, I didn't quite understand . . ." I faltered, but his voice was hurt.

"Be more than sorry. Be charitable. You've raised your voice in my behalf—now raise your prejudices."

"I don't . . ."

"You will. Now," he said brusquely, "here's my proposition. I want to give you a gift, open, above-board, no strings attached and certainly no soul involved. Collect when you like."

It was so much like a dream, that wide, drowsy street, green under the trees, the laughter of girls on nearby porches, the tap of horses' hooves as a carriage drove past, a dream and yet so real! He wasn't at all what I'd always expected him to be. He was so—well, sincere.

"But why," I said slowly, staring surreptitiously at his head and the hidden pink horns. "Why a gift?"

"We went through that. You stood up for me."

"Really," I murmured, "I didn't mean to." Trying to disclaim what I had done made me feel ashamed of myself.

There was a long silence, then he picked up a pebble and tossed it into the road. "The horns are easy to hide," he said irrelevantly, "but the tail is the very devil." He laughed at his own joke. "I have to tuck it between my legs and it gives me something of a pot belly here in front. I'm rather vain about my figure . . ." His voice trailed away. After a moment he went on, switching to what seemed to be another irrelevancy. "We're entering a century of enlightenment, achievement is the word. Progress. That big steel bridge they're building in New York, steel and stone and how long before they fly and after that, what? The planets? The stars?" He sighed. "Civilization bubbles like a glass of beer with a head of technical advances. But what about the body, the culture of the nation, the moral values and standards?" He wet his lips. "All that talk of beer! Are you old enough to have a glass?"

"Of course," I said indignantly. Then I frowned, "It's sort of—well, strange, hearing you talk about moral values and standards."

He shrugged and stood up, giving me his hand to help me to my feet. "You all right now?"

"I guess so."

We walked along slowly, past the residential section of town and out along Main Street. "I've always been concerned with moral values. Let morality go hang and where would I be. . . . But your defense of me, you think you didn't mean it, yet subconsciously you did. Freud hasn't fully developed it yet, but most of it is there. Subconsciously you believed what you said or you'd never have said it. I know a defense when I hear one. Ah! Flanagan's Saloon." He pushed open the swinging doors and I looked around guiltily, then followed him in, hoping I wouldn't be recognized. The bartender, however, hardly even noticed me. In the corner someone was playing a soft sad song on a piano that needed tuning.

"Now the gift I had planned is a sort of perennial youth."

"Perennial youth?"

"Obviously, I won't offer you anything as rare as immortality, even to the ends of time as we know it. That's rather grandiose. Oh, not that I haven't done it; but then it's for payment received, and there are all sorts of ritualistic deals involved."

"You mean my soul?"

His hand tightened around the beer. "Prejudice," he murmured softly. "No. Again you wouldn't understand. Eternal youth, I call that gift, and it's rather a chimera. This one is a cosmetic approach. I can't extend your lifetime. After all . . ." he shrugged expressively. "But while you live I'll make you look like seventeen and feel like seventeen, with the body of a seventeen-year-old." He smiled a bit wickedly over his beer, "And of course, the libido of a seventeen-year-old."

I felt my ears redden. There was a sore point. How many nights had I lain awake, my whole body burning with unconsummated desire? Oh no, I wouldn't buy that. What a terrible trap!

I shook my head. "I'm a kid. No matter how I throw my weight around, I'm still a kid. I have to fight for respect, watch my step with the older guys and as for the girls I want . . ." I thought of Peggy Talbert, "Well, they don't see me for dust. Not at seventeen."

He sipped the beer slowly. "It doesn't have to be seventeen. Suppose I came back ten years from now. By then you'll be ready for it."

"Ten years." I nodded. "That would do it. By then I'd know enough. I'd really be a man." Twenty-seven was·just right. I smiled at him to take the sting away from my doubt. "No strings?"

"Really!" He seemed hazy all of a sudden, almost translucent. His lips pouted and I could hear a whispered, "Prejudice," in a bitter tone. Then everything about him, except the pout, was gone and finally that drifted away too and I just sat there, staring at the two beers. At least till the bartender spotted me and thundered out, "Eddie Kovacs? What are you doing here? Beat it before the cops get after me."

I hurried out, my beer hardly tasted, and I walked down the street in a haze of bewilderment.

It was exactly ten years. I had been out of law school for three years and I was practicing on East Barrow Street in my home town, Wisnesh Falls. Sam Rosen, Dick Parks, and myself, we had all gone through school together and now we shared a set of offices, four rooms in a row. You had to go through Sam's office to get to Dick's, and through Sam's and Dick's to get to mine. Someday, we told ourselves, we'd have a place with all our rooms off a central hall, and Lilly Esteber would be in the hall instead of the fourth office. Lilly was the secretary-typist for Rosen, Parks and Kovacs, Attorneys-at-Law, and also the object of bitter competition between Sam and Dick. Myself, I had been married to Mary for three years now and we had two little boys, but I could still appreciate Lilly's pretty blond looks as well as her efficient work.

Well, it was after five and I had just leaned back with a cigar in my mouth for that moment of rest before I left the office. I was fumbling in my pocket for a match when there was a flare of light in front of my eyes. I drew back, and then felt cold down the length of my spine. He was sitting there, dressed in black, quite stylish, with a black Homburg on his head and black velvet lapels to his suit. His finger was extended and it was burning with a clear blue light. I think that little touch of fantasy was just enough to keep me from being too shaken. I wet my lips and glanced quickly at the door.

"Well, light the cigar and if anyone comes in I'm just a client."

I lit the cigar, trying to keep my hand steady. Then it had happened. It really had!

"You're probably surprised to see me."

"Surprised is hardly a word that fits. If Dick or Sam comes in, how can I explain you?"

"You'll think of something. That's what makes a successful lawyer, the ability to think on your feet, and you're headed for success."

I forgot everything in the face of that remark. "Can you see the future?" I asked eagerly.

"Now, now." He took a cigar from my desk and lit it with his finger, then blew out the flame. "That's rather a showy stunt but I like it. See the future indeed! You have very little knowledge of time and space. The future isn't, my dear boy. It just isn't. How can I see it?"

"But you said . . ."

"An educated guess based on your progress, your aggressive personality, and your adjusted view of life. Oh, I've checked up on you and I'm very satisfied, very. You're doing quite nicely."

"I've done it on my own," I said defensively.

"Indeed you have. At any rate, are you ready for my gift?"

"Ready? Well, I never thought of it these past ten years. I suppose I didn't really believe it had happened and I've had so much to do . . ."

"Haven't we all?"

"I'm twenty-seven. I'd stay like this forever?"

"Correction, till you die. Forever is eternal youth, remember? You'll die at the age you normally would, seventy or eighty, but till then you'll look and feel twenty-seven."

"Still, twenty-seven is so young, young in terms of my profession. You see, what future is there for a twenty-seven-year-old, in law? I'd still be the junior partner. Politics—well, I've had my eye on politics for a while now. The machine in this city is so basically rotten. What I'd like to see . . ."

He listened carefully, shaking his head and now and then asking pointed, discerning questions. He genuinely cared what I was doing, what my plans were, and I felt his personal concern with a warm pleasure. In the last few years, I suddenly realized, I had made almost no real friends. Even Dick and Sam went their separate ways. They respected me, yes, but how much feeling was there behind the respect?

He looked at his watch and I broke off. "I'm sorry—boring you like this."

"Boring me? Ridiculous! I'm fascinated. I just checked to see if you wouldn't be late for dinner. Perhaps you'd better call Mary."

I had forgotten completely! I called and made some vague excuse, telling her I'd probably miss supper. When I hung up he looked at me keenly.

"You do that a lot."

"What?"

"Miss supper."

"Well, yes. I work hard though. It's not . . ." I winced as I thought of an unhappy scene with Mary last week. "Well, it's just business."

"Watch it though," he said kindly. "This devotion to work and success is the quickest way to ruin a marriage. I know. Now you have ambition, use it, but don't neglect the family." He ground out his cigar and started to become vague. Alarmed, I cried out, "Where are you going?"

He paused, a smoky ghost of a man, his voice thin but clear. "Spatially, that's hard to answer. The necessary physics haven't yet been worked out. I assume it's a coexisting plane of being, impinging on this world but not a part of it . . ."

"No, no," I stood up, "I mean, why are you going, so soon?"

"For a lawyer your thinking is a bit muddled." He chuckled and adjusted his suit, smoothing down the lapels. "You've made your decision. I'll be back in ten years."

I sat back as he vanished. "In ten years," I whispered. My own cigar had gone out and I tried to light it but I remembered the flame on his finger and I shivered, then put the dead cigar down.

I heard the door open and Lilly looked in. "Still here, Ed? I was locking up."

"I'll put the lights out." She looked around the office and sniffed. "Have you been playing with matches? There's a queer smell here."

"Is there? I hadn't noticed."

She sighed and left and I sat for a long time staring into space.

Thirty-seven, a good, robust age for a political figure. Mayor? Governor? Why not? He had said I was going far, that I would be successful. Surely he knew, in spite of his double talk about time. If I believed in the devil why not believe in prescience?

And I believed in the devil.

The year I was thirty-seven, I introduced what was probably the soundest piece of legislation on labor unions to be heard in Congress. It was defeated by an overwhelming majority, but the papers—oh how they played it up.

"Surely the most promising congressman this war-weary nation has yet produced," Mary read from the late edition of Washington's biggest newspaper. "Now what do you say to that."

"Fellow constituents . . ."

"Oh God!" My eleven-year-old boy threw up his hands. Alice, aged nine, looked at me witheringly. "Not another speech!"

Helplessly I turned to Mary. "A man is never a hero in his own home."

She was flipping through the paper, but was suddenly stopped by the drama page. "Well! Look what musical comedy is opening!"

They clustered around her, three blond heads, Mary's in the center, and I looked at them proudly, then past them to the long window opening on the portico of our impressive Washington home. He was standing there, hands behind his back, staring out at the green sweep of lawn and the Potomac in the background. I swallowed and turned back to Mary and the kids. "I'll be back in a moment," I murmured, but they were too absorbed to pay attention.

"You haven't changed," I said as I walked up to him.

"Should I have? Some things are timeless."

"Or outside of time."

He turned quickly, giving me that shy but open smile that had first captivated me. "Well, Ed. Thirty-seven and the most promising Congressman. Think of it."

I sighed. "I've done little else."

"You've thought of me too."

"Yes, I have, on and off these ten years. Not merely the implication of your gift, but that it should be vouchsafed to me—I've faced my own growing maturity with an equally growing wonder."

He frowned. "I don't know if I like what time is doing to you."

"I beg your pardon?"

"Pomposity should never be confused with wisdom. You try too hard. Come, let's take a walk."

For a while we walked in silence. My feelings were hurt, but in all fairness he was right. Finally he said, "Ed, I'm glad you're straightened out with Mary."

I looked at him quickly. "We're very much in love."

"That's good." The corner of his smile was a little crooked. Sardonic? "Politically expedient too?"

"I love Mary."

"I suppose you do. By the way, whatever happened to Lilly, your pretty little secretary?"

"She's still my pretty little secretary. Dick and Sam lost out on that."

He nodded thoughtfully. "Seriously, you're headed up, Ed, and I'm glad."

I said, "Thanks," and for a while we walked on together. Then tentatively he began, "About my gift . . ."

I pointed across the rooftops to where the dome of the Capitol rose up. "I still don't want to be the kid in Congress. I suppose I should say yes—"

"Why not? You could dye your hair grey, a little makeup . . ."

"And Mary? Could I fool her and my kids with makeup?"

"But what a waste, Ed, what a waste."

"No, not really." I stood up straight, my shoulders back and my jaw firm. "Maturity is in the man, not in the body."

"Whatever that means." He shook his head sadly. "You must curb this tendency to pompousness. It sticks out like a sore thumb, and eventually it's bound to backfire."

I shrugged in embarrassment. "Well, you take on a certain style in the political rat-race . . ." My voice trailed off.

He patted my arm. "Now, now. You're doing fine. I did think thirty-seven a well-rounded age. Mature and yet not old, a man's most vigorous time."

He smiled deprecatingly. "Myself, I stopped at thirty-seven."

I glanced at his sharply etched profile, the noble lift to the brow, the black eyes and the touch of sadness. "For you, yes," I said slowly, "but you're not tied up with politics."

"Am I not?" He wet his lips with a too pink tongue.

"Well, you know in what sense I mean."

He sighed and shoved his hat back, the two pink horns pushing up in front of it. "In ten years."

I watched him fade, wondering with a strange sense of loss if I had done the right thing!

The next time I saw him was the year after that very bitter, very brutal compaign where I lost the presidential nomination. *The Boy Candidate.* The head of my own party had come out with a devastating statement a week before the primary. "In my opinion, Kovacs has plenty to learn yet!"

But then he always had hated my guts, ever since that blow-up on the labor union scandal.

I lost Mary that winter, and with her all direction, all purpose, seemed to go out of my life. Even the children couldn't reach me. The very act of living was an effort; indeed I hardly think I would have gone on if it hadn't been for Lilly's untiring devotion.

I was going back to Kansas in the club car when I realized that Satan was sitting beside me. "It's guilt, really," he said with no preamble. "Actually, you feel that in some way you're responsible for Mary's death, that you've failed her."

"Go to the devil," I said.

"I don't know quite how to answer that." He smiled tolerantly. "Now come Ed, we've always been friends."

I looked at him distastefully. "If I've learned one thing in forty-seven years, it's the meaningless quality of friendship."

"Oh, but you're thinking of your political friends, each with his own ax to grind. True friendship asks nothing. Like mine—and Lilly's. Indeed it gives."

"Leave Lilly out of it."

"That's right out of an old melodrama. Ed, is forty-seven the age?"

"Forty-seven is hell," I said through clenched teeth. "Let me go on. What, by all that's holy, have I got at this age to make me cling to it?"

"How you mix your figures of speech, and I can't begin to answer by anything holy. Yours is not the first tragedy of all time," he added with some asperity.

I looked at him broodingly. He was still dressed in the latest style, black but not somber, not at all somber. "How is your research with time and space?"

He looked blank, then laughed. "I don't research it Ed, I live it. You should look up some of those English astronomers, some fascinating ideas about the cosmos. Wouldn't He be amazed!" He shook his head, "Ed, I hate to see you like this. Destroyed, running away from Washington."

"It's only a visit," I said stiffly. I looked out the window for a moment, then burst out, "You know what he said, I 'have plenty to learn yet!' And that damned cartoonist on the Star did a picture of me playing with alphabet blocks, spelling out *economy*."

Satan chuckled. "Where's your sense of humor? Good heavens, Ed, beat them at their own game. Be the perennial boy candidate. I'll help."

"No thanks," I said stiffly, "I'll keep on."

"You have a Freudian fear of youth."

"And you have an unhealthy taste for snap analysis."

He slowly shook his head and pursed his lips. "We're just not hitting it off this time. In ten years."

In ten years! And I turned back to the window, broodingly.

"Surely," Satan said coaxingly, "you'll stop now."

"But what have I to gain?" I poured two glasses of brandy and handed one to him. He stared at it speculatively. "This is a pretty stiff shot."

Surprised, I looked at the amber liquor. "It's a good brandy— damned good, and with the Germans marching into France, God knows when we'll see another bottle of it."

"I liked the speech you made the other day about appeasement. You've gotten over that old tendency to pontificate."

"Well, thank you." I smiled at him fondly . . . "And you seem to have changed too. There's—well, a more human quality to you, and that's surprising. I had an idea you were changeless."

"Nothing is. You should know that," he said reprovingly. "Besides, in times like these we cannot exist in a changeless state."

"Now *you've* taken to pontification." I reached out and put my hand on his arm. "Don't be offended, I was joking. But . . . well, damn it man, aren't you confused about whose side you're on?"

"I'm not one bit confused," he snapped. Then he sipped at his brandy. "It is good, though I can't abide drinking it from a tumbler."

"Lilly has some brandy snifters somewhere, but I think they've been made into planters."

He shuddered, then sipped at his drink again. "How is Lilly?"

"Lovely, as all brides are."

"Which brings me to the point of my visit. You're fifty-seven, close to sixty. Isn't it time you accepted my gift? This psychological procrastination . . ."

"I hear that word psychological so often now, Satan. There's nothing psychological about it, nor is it procrastination."

"Then what is it?"

"Possibly it's human. Shall I take your gift now and cheat myself out of the most valuable thing left to me, my golden years as the sage of the party, the wise old man of American politics?"

"You're mocking me."

I looked up quickly. "Me? Mock at you? On my honor, I never would." I shook my head. "No, these years are suddenly terribly precious, the only real completion to my life."

"But Lilly . . ."

"Yes, but Lilly. Shall I let her walk on alone?"

"Still," there was a touch of coldness in his voice. A rejected gift hardly makes for friendship. "There is the matter of health. You've been blessed with the constitution of an ox, but you'll begin to run down soon."

"We all do," I said with a shrug.

He looked at the liquor. "I should suspect your liver will go first."

I chuckled. "Hardly. Isn't it usually the arteries?"

He threw up his hands. "I shall never understand humans."

I lifted my eyebrows, "Nor I devils." As he started to fade away I said, "Will I see you again?"

His eyes, so black and deep, studied mine and then he smiled softly, "I hope so, dear friend."

"Whistling," I said, staring into the fire, "is a lost art."

Satan smiled tolerantly. "A philosopher at seventy-seven. Is that your ambition?"

"In part. But you know, when I was a boy everybody whistled. You whistled at night, walking home. You whistled about the house. You whistled while you walked along. You even whistled in the shower."

"And now."

"Whoever whistles now? It's a lost art." I looked at him quizzically. "I missed you the last time around."

"I knew you wouldn't accept it."

"And now?"

"Call it a friendship call."

"Meaning you're pretty sure I won't be around ten years from now."

With a show of annoyance he said, "I once told you I couldn't see the future."

"So you did, but we're back on time again. It evidently passes more slowly for me. I have trouble remembering from ten years to ten years."

"You keep a diary."

"Of course, but I never read it. What's dead is dead. So in the end your gift failed."

"You didn't accept it, but it was always waiting."

Curiously I added, "Have you ever offered this to others?"

He smiled broadly. "How do you imagine so many movie stars stay so suspiciously young till the end?"

"But again, to beat an old bone, what do you gain?"

"Are we to have that prejudice again? Are you still afraid for your soul?"

"Have I one?"

"That's not for me to say." He moved the blanket over my feet. "Where's Lilly?"

"Baby-sitting with a great-grandchild."

"And so you have your wish—the grand old man of American politics. You look the part too."

I ran my hand self-consciously through my mane of silver hair. "Now who's mocking?"

"So your memory is clear."

"As clear as a bell."

He stood up, slim and young in a new Continental cut, black suit, the pants skin tight, the three button jacket fitting like a glove, and he straightened his black hat, then patted his stomach below the belt. "That tail still gives me a pot."

I chuckled softly. "If the pants were a bit looser you could run it down one leg."

He pursed his lips. "I stay in style, but who knows . . . it's a thought for another age." He put his hand on my arm. "I must go, I have so much work to do."

"I wonder about that work," I said gently.

He smiled, so sad and knowing a smile, and again I looked into his black eyes and beyond to—what? Nothing?

"Goodbye," I said softly, and I knew it was goodbye.

C. S. FORESTER

The Bedchamber Mystery

Now THAT A HUNDRED YEARS have passed one of the scandals in my family can be told. It is very doubtful if in 1843 Miss Forester (she was Eulalie, but being the eldest daughter unmarried, she of course was Miss Forester) and Miss Emily Forester and Miss Eunice Forester ever foresaw the world of 1943 to which their story would be told; in fact it is inconceivable that they could have believed that there ever would be a world in which their story could be told blatantly in public print. At that time it was the sort of thing that could only be hinted at in whispers during confidential moments in feminine drawing rooms; but it was whispered about enough to reach in the end the ears of my grandfather, who was their nephew, and my grandfather told it to me.

In 1843 Miss Forester and Miss Emily and Miss Eunice Forester were already maiden ladies of a certain age. The old-fashioned Georgian house in which they lived kept itself modestly retired, just like its inhabitants, from what there was of bustle and excitement in the High Street of the market town. The ladies indeed led a retired life; they went to church a little, they visited those of the sick whom it was decent and proper for maiden ladies to visit, they read the more colorless of the novels in the circulating library, and sometimes they entertained other ladies at tea.

And once a week they entertained a man. It might almost be said that they went from week to week looking forward to those evenings. Dr. Acheson was (not one of the old ladies would have been heartless enough to say "fortunately," but each of them felt it) a widower, and several years older even than my great-great-aunt Eulalie. Moreover, he was a keen whist player and a brilliant one, but in no way keener or more brilliant than were Eulalie, Emily, and Eunice. For years now the three nice old ladies had looked forward to their weekly evening of whist—all the ritual of setting out the green table, the two hours of silent cut-and-thrust play, and the final twenty minutes of conversation with Dr. Acheson as he drank a glass of old Madeira before bidding them good night.

The late Mrs. Acheson had passed to her Maker somewhere about 1830, so that it was for thirteen years they had played their weekly game of whist before the terrible thing happened. To this day we do not know whether it happened to Eulalie or Emily or Eunice, but it happened to one of them. The three of them had retired for the night, each to her separate room, and had progressed far toward the final stage of getting into bed. They were not dried-up old spinsters; on the contrary, they were women of weight and substance, with the buxom contours even married women might have been proud of. It was her weight which was the undoing of one of them, Eulalie, Emily, or Eunice.

Through the quiet house that bedtime there sounded the crash of china and a cry of pain, and two of the sisters—which two we do not know—hurried in their dressing gowns to the bedroom of the third—her identity is uncertain—to find her bleeding profusely from severe cuts in the lower part of the back. The jagged china fragments had inflicted severe wounds, and, most unfortunately, just in those parts where the injured sister could not attend to them herself. Under the urgings of the other two she fought down her modesty sufficiently to let them attempt to deal with them, but the bleeding was profuse, and the blood of the Foresters streamed from the prone figure face downward on the bed in terrifying quantity.

"We shall have to send for the doctor," said one of the ministering sisters. It was a shocking thing to contemplate.

"Oh, but we cannot!" said the other ministering sister.

"We must," said the first.

"How terrible!" said the second.

And with that the injured sister twisted her neck and joined in the conversation. "I will not have the doctor," she said. "I would die of shame."

"Think of the disgrace of it!" said the second sister. "We might even have to explain to him how it happened!"

"But she's bleeding to death," protested the first sister.

"I'd rather die!" said the injured one, and then, as a fresh appalling thought struck her, she twisted her neck even further. "I could never face him again. And what would happen to our whist?"

That was an aspect of the case which until then had occurred to neither of the other sisters, and it was enough to make them blench. But they were of stern stuff. Just as we do not know which was the injured one, we do not know which one thought of a way out of the difficulty, and we shall never know. We know that it was Miss Eulalie, as befitted her rank as eldest sister, who called to Deborah, the maid, to go and fetch Dr. Acheson at once, but that does not mean to say that it was not Miss Eulalie who was the injured sister—injured or not, Miss Eulalie was quite capable of calling to Deborah and telling her what to do.

As she was bid, Deborah went and fetched Dr. Acheson and conducted him to Miss Eunice's bedroom, but of course the fact that it was Miss Eunice's bedroom is really no indication that it was Miss Eunice who was in there. Dr. Acheson had no means of knowing; all he saw was a recumbent form covered by a sheet. In the center of the sheet a round hole a foot in diameter had been cut, and through the hole the seat of the injury was visible.

Dr. Acheson needed no explanations. He took his needles and

his thread from his little black bag and he set to work and sewed up the worst of the cuts and attended to the minor ones. Finally he straightened up and eased his aching back.

"I shall have to take those stitches out," he explained to the still and silent figure which had borne the stitching stoically without a murmur. "I shall come next Wednesday and do that."

Until next Wednesday the three Misses Forester kept to their rooms. Not one of them was seen in the streets of the market town, and when on Wednesday Dr. Acheson knocked at the door Deborah conducted him once more to Miss Eunice's bedroom. There was the recumbent form, and there was the sheet with the hole in it. Dr. Acheson took out the stitches.

"It has healed very nicely," said Dr. Acheson. "I don't think any further attention from me will be necessary."

The figure under the sheet said nothing, nor did Dr. Acheson expect it. He gave some concluding advice and went his way. He was glad later to receive a note penned in Miss Forester's Italian hand:

DEAR DR. ACHESON,

We will all be delighted if you will come to whist this week as usual.

When Dr. Acheson arrived he found that the "as usual" applied only to his coming, for there was a slight but subtle change in the furnishings of the drawing room. The stiff, high-backed chairs on which the three Misses Forester sat bore, each of them, a thick and comfortable cushion upon the seat. There was no knowing which of the sisters needed it.

ASHLEY MONTAGU AND EDWARD DARLING

Beliefs About the
Human Body

THERE IS A COMPLETE ROLLICKING CHAPTER on Victorian attitudes toward the body and the language with which such a society was able to survive, given those attitudes. We've all heard how legs became parts of furniture only or, better still, unmentioned except as limbs, and how the artist at the dinner party dared to ask for some of the breast instead of saying "white meat" and was permanently ostracized. Perhaps the best-known case is the experience of Peter Simple in Captain Marryat's novel of that name first published in 1834. The incident took place in the Barbados:

Supper was now announced, and having danced the last country dance with Miss Minerva, I of course had the pleasure of handing her into the supper-room. It was my fate to sit opposite to a fine turkey, and I asked my partner if I should have the pleasure of helping her to a piece of the breast. She looked at me very indignantly, and said, "Curse your impudence, sar, I wonder where you larn manners. Sar, I take a lilly turkey *bosom,* if you please. Talk of breast to a lady, sar; really quite horrid.

There was a story about a finishing school for young ladies which was visited by a distinguished French statesman of the period; when the headmistress guided him upstairs to see the layout

184

of the dormitory facilities, a little group of girls happened to be in the upper hall and, seeing the visitor, ran screaming away, presumably with their skirts over their faces, yelling, "A man! A man!" Indeed, it was not many years ago that the words *naked* and *nude* were judged to have Fescennine implications. One recalls a "Something-or-Other Revisited" article, no doubt by Perelman, in which the writer remembers that as a boy he thought women were solid from shoulders down past hips and thigh to the floor itself and only later learned that the little rascals are the same bifurcated creatures that the rest of us are.

So we denied the existence of the body; and yet somehow the race did not die out. Somebody must have squealed.

If our first thoughts are of sustenance, surely our next thoughts must be about the amusing and endlessly interesting bodies we inhabit for some years. Nowhere is the prevalence of nonsense more dominant than in the innumerable misconceptions about the human body. Brace yourself for some real air pockets.

Oh, Those Baby-Blue Eyes!

Yes, it is true that all newborn babies, even Negro babies, have blue eyes. The reason for this is that all babies lack pigment of any kind in the layer of specialized tissue of the iris where pigment will later appear. But the idea that the color of a person's eyes is due to the color of the pigment in them—as is generally believed—is totally false. In no eyes of any living soul is there anything approaching a blue-colored pigment.

The truth is that eye color is due to two principal conditions: one, the physical character of the pigment itself; two, the optical phenomenon of interference. There are pigments in the eye, all right—but they are not blue pigments, not ever. The pigments of the eye lie chiefly in the iris; and the iris consists of several layers of specialized tissues, each of which plays its part in determining what color people will say your eyes are. Sometimes the outer layer of the iris is the only one containing pigment cells. But as a rule pigment cells of various kinds are contained in the stromal (basal) layer of the iris. These, together with the nature of the light acting upon them, yield the color effect. Let a bluish light or a reflected blue from a shirt, tie, or dress become active near a blue-eyed person and watch those eyes deepen! How many thrones have toppled because of the interaction of these phenomena.

The blue appearance of the eyes is actually produced by the refraction of light from *brown* pigment particles at the back of the iris. It is very much like the blue veins in your skin—which are really full of dark-red blood; but seen through the skin they do not look that way except in rare and distractingly repulsive instances such as the red nose on the drunk. In blue-eyed people there is an absence of brown pigment in the basal layer—and that is why the babies always are born with blue eyes, as we said.

Thus the color of the eyes is dependent on the refractive capacities of the pigments—the absorptive and reflective qualities—and not on the colors of the pigments themselves.

All this changes, of course, with the use of contact lenses. It used to be that no man, by taking thought, could either add a cubit to his stature nor change the color of his eyes. Those, indeed, were the days.

Hair on the Chest Means Strength?

Let the gentlemen with no hirsute decorations on the chest take comfort from this: Dr. James B. Hamilton of the Yale School of Medicine administered male sex hormones to men who had failed to mature sexually, and they became bald. From this Dr. Hamilton concluded that baldness, and not hairiness, is a sign of mature masculinity. Hence, those persons who associated what they believed to be one of the qualities of the gorilla, a hairy chest, with that other well-known quality of the gorilla, brute strength, were making an erroneous association; but they were doing more than that: they should brush up on their gorillas. These jungle beasts have almost no hair on the chest at all, and though they are preternaturally strong, they are not brutal. They have plenty everywhere else—belly, back, shoulders, arms, and legs—but none on the chest.

"My brother Esau is an hairy man, but I am a smooth man." Yes, and who walked off with the loot?

This myth of the significance of hairiness ties in with another popular mistake: that baldness may be caused by excessive thought —an idea reflected in the contemporary vernacular "egghead" for "professor." Many great thinkers have been bald. Many non-thinkers also have been—and are—bald. The thought processes have nothing whatever to do with the hair-growing processes, of course. However, if we follow Dr. Hamilton's line of thought, it is possible to derive an enchanting explanation for the use of bald men: maturity of masculinity is shown by this very characteristic of baldness. Hence one might say that the bald are mature; and the mature, of course, are thinkers. Harumpf, or words to that effect.

Crowding of the Teeth Is a Human Development?

Every so often one reads that the orthodontist is prospering as never before because the jaws of man are growing smaller and there is not enough room in them for his teeth to erupt properly, and so they become crowded and maloccluded. There is no truth whatsoever in these notions. Man's earliest representatives, the Australopithecines, in several instances exhibited crowded teeth. As our leading authority, Professor Adolph H. Schultz, has stated, "Unequivocal crowding of teeth is quite common among recent wild monkeys and apes. I have never failed to encounter cases with displaced, twisted, or impacted single or several large teeth in collections of primate skulls, and often such manifestations of unmistakable maladjustment in the size of the teeth and the jaws, resulting in crowding, are much more pronounced than in the two or three instances found in the Austroalpithecines. Crowded premolars are particularly frequent in all manlike apes and comparatively rare in monkeys. Moderate to very marked irregularities in the alignment of the incisors are surprisingly common among baboons and not at all rare in most other species of recent monkeys as well as apes." Such cases seem to result from insufficiently large bony spaces between the incisors and the canines (eye-teeth). Crowding of permanent teeth is frequently associated with delays in the shedding and replacement of milk teeth.

PALE SKIN MEANS ANEMIA?

Persons in perfect health often have pale skins, and this is because the amount of pigment in the epidermis and the supply of blood to the various layers of the outer skin are less than in persons having more coloring. It usually has nothing to do with health if we are pale. The blood supply may be diffuse rather than concentrated—but that's merely an individual difference and is not connected with health one way or the other. In cases of anemia there is a great reduction in the number of red blood cells—and this, too, causes paleness. Ordinarily, eating liver readily cures such a condition. Hence the familiar judgment that "she has anemia because she is pale" is likely to be completely wrong. That is not the test.

ROSY CHEEKS MEAN GOOD HEALTH?

Our literature abounds with evidence that bouncing, energetic, barefoot-boy-type good health is characterized by ruddy cheeks and sparkling eyes; and apparently the male of our species has—with rare exceptions—found the vigorous and high-colored female more exciting and attractive than any pale substitute. This may be due to the fact, as some writers have suggested, that blood is the symbol of life (one recalls that in the days of the Four Humors, the sanguine man was an optimist); but perhaps it is more likely to have evolved through experience: the girl with the quick color played a more vivacious game of tag than the anemic and prissy cousin. In any event, history records that the pale ones have always tried to find ways to add a little color—and sometimes quite a lot of color; and they wouldn't go to all that trouble just for fun. (The exceptions have been in occasional cultures where

the highborn lady was very delicate and quick to faint if some
ruffian exposed his vulgarity by pronouncing the word *leg,* as
among the pale Victorians; or among the lovesick in the days of
Courtly Love—their pallid skin showed that they were suffering
for love's sake and of course this made them irresistibly attractive.)

The high color may or may not be a sign of good health. In the
case of a person with a low-grade, continuous fever, caused by
some chronic infection, the skin may be beautifully pink and
white and the eyes most luminous. Certain forms of tuberculosis
and heart disease are associated with high color; and this is true
also for some disorders of the circulatory system. Hence one cannot always assume the leaping vitality from the rosiness of the
cheek; but what one can assume is that the chromatically meri-
torious angels will never lack for interesting pursuit, be they
healthy or otherwise.

A Brainy Child More Delicate Than the Moron?

Many a protective mother, in order to prevent her little genius
from submitting himself—or herself—to the risks of rough-and-
tumble play that seems to be native to "normal" children, imagines
that the brilliant child is, in fact, physically weaker, and that this
is to be expected: she may even develop the alleged delicacy into
an indication of superior status. "My little Ermintrude cannot go
on those long hikes—she is too delicate. But she gets A's in all
her courses, and she is a regular prodigy on the piano."

To which, other things being equal, the proper response is a
firm but simple "Balderdash."

Bright children are neither stronger nor weaker than average
children. But it is easy to see how the idea takes root. An average
child with a weak heart, for instance, could be advised not to play
jump rope or tag until the heart strengthens. Meanwhile the child
gets a lot of adult attention and spends a good deal of time in-
doors—with books, musical instruments, or other civilizing play-
things. Naturally, then, this child gains proficiency in the cultural
fields, which the other child, outdoors with the jump rope, does

not. But the brilliance has nothing to do with the physical stamina, nor the strength with the brightness.

HANDLING TOADS PRODUCES WARTS?

Mankind has long associated filth and dirt and venom with toads and snakes, both of which are surprisingly clean creatures. The old woodcuts of Antichrist showed the fiend spitting out toads and snakes. The attitude constitutes a dastardly canard which should be vigorously rejected by all toad and snake lovers, if any. Warts are invariably produced by an infectious filterable virus that produces the well-known localized overgrowth of the horny layer of the skin that we call a wart. The virus, as is not generally known, is communicable from person to person by touch. The best removal technique appears to be through X-ray treatment. But neither as a curse of God nor as a result of handling toads are warts produced, and to imagine otherwise is to exchange the scientific method for the ancient imitative magic of the primitive. Yet thousands of people continue to credit the ancient and utterly false association of the bumpy toad with the bumpy human skin. Nothing to it. Toads are delightful comrades, and do not have to be taught not to talk.

FEEDING THE SKIN—FROM THE OUTSIDE

In our days at least one entire industry depends upon the belief of the ladies that the skin can be nourished by the application of certain oils and creams to the surface. The same industry is beginning to get a good deal of support from the male section also, according to recent reports.

We hate to be a spoilsport about it, and certainly you are not going to do yourself any harm if you want to put on the oils. But the fact is—in case anybody is interested—that the human skin is nourished from the same sources as is all the rest of the body: through the nutrients carried in the blood stream. The skin is no more benefited, actually, by the surface application of creams and oils than the brain or the heart would be from similar treatment.

If we really wanted to play the Calamity Jane role, we could point out that too much use of creams and oils can be truly dangerous—if their use occludes many of the pores of the skin through which the natural oils of the skin emerge.

No doubt about it, one can satisfy oneself that one has made the skin less dry, at least for the time being, by applying cosmetics of one kind or another; and temporarily one has done so. But for normal people the secretions of the skin glands supply the only lubrication that is needed. Check with the family doctor for details.

Why Do Women Have One Rib More Than Men?

This question was asked seriously by a Sunday-school teacher in a Bible Belt fundamentalist classroom, and it was asked for a perfectly good reason: the teacher wanted to find out if the children had learned their lesson as set forth in Genesis 2:21—"And the Lord God caused a deep sleep to fall upon Adam, and he slept; and he took one of his ribs, and closed up the flesh instead thereof; and the rib, which the Lord God had taken from man, made he a woman, and brought her unto the man." So the gold star for the day went to the little student who explained this event.

We know, of course, that women have precisely the same number of ribs that men do—twelve pairs—and that they are not in the least different from male ribs in any respect. But let's not get smug about it, because it is a fact that the female often has one coccygeal, or "tail," vertebra less than the male. If you ask us, the whole business of tail vertebrae in humans is pretty ridiculous, but there you are.

Nervousness Means Weak Nerves?

The term *nervousness* refers in a crude (not precise) way to a purely psychological state which has no connection at all with the structure of the nerve fibers. Unless it has been subjected to a partial destruction, there is no such thing as a "weak" nerve. And even if a nerve had suffered partial destruction of its substance, there would usually be no reason to associate this with nervousness. Our "nervousness" is a catchall phrase of popular leveling which really describes nothing specifically. A horse with a sensitive mouth shows its distaste for the bridle and rider by annoying sidestepping. The horse is "nervous." A boy ordered to the principal's office for infraction of school rules is full of fear as to the consequences. He is "nervous." A housewife is tired after a full day of cleaning, cooking, and a meeting of the PTA. She is "nervous." Every one of us is nervous in that we react to nerve stimuli. Weak nerve tissue has nothing to do with it.

My Feet Are Killing Me!

If people are going to insist on walking around on two feet instead of four—and it begins to look as if the habit is here to stay—then they have got to put up with tired feet from time to time, especially if they are overweight, a condition which also seems to be here to stay. But the extremely popular notion that the pain is caused by fallen arches, or even by falling arches, is some miles from the truth. Let's see, now:

The arch of the foot is made up chiefly of the tarsal and metatarsal bones. These are united to one another by numerous ligaments of such noble strength—and the bones are arched by nature in such a way—that the arch itself is never going to collapse. Relax: the arch is there to stay.

If there is any collapse in there—and this could happen—it will be the tendons of the sole of the foot, the plantar aponeurosis. In such a case, the foot tends to flatten out and we recognize the fall of the secondary, or soft-tissue, arch. But this is not the bone-and-ligament foundation, which is what most people mean when they talk of fallen arches.

We must not allow ourselves to be carried away. It is not *impossible* that a complete and hopeless breakdown could occur—one could have faulty bone structure or something. But the condition is all but unknown, as Dr. D. J. Morton, late associate professor of anatomy at Columbia University, made plain; and he was one of America's leading authorities on the feet.

Hair Turns Gray Overnight?

Even medical men have fallen for this one; and of course every close reader of horror stories is aware that "when they forced open the bedroom door the next morning, Lord Cholmondeley's hair had turned pure white." The fallacy is so deeply rooted in our folklore that we find even the hard-bitten editors of *Time* magazine indulging in it. Witness Ernie Pyle's story in the issue of May 31, 1943: "Several weeks before Tunisia fell to the Allies, reporter Pyle went into battle with the infantry. . . . He returned to the rear a little grayer." Capping the climax was an eighteenth-century ghost story that we hope was intended satirically: it told of a guest at the old castle, a young man who was totally indifferent to ghosts, who agreed to sleep in the haunted chamber. He placed his brown wig on one of the uprights of the four-poster and left the room to perform his ablutions. Returning, he found that his door had closed and locked. Since it was rather late, he shrugged and settled down for the night outside in the hall. In the morning when they broke open the door for him they found that his wig had turned pure snowy white.

In *The Prisoner of Chillon* (1816) Byron resumes the myth:

> My hair is gray, but not with years,
>   Nor grew it white
>   In a single night,
> As men's have grown from sudden fears.

We were serious when we said "even medical men." Listen to Lee McCarthy, M.D., writing in a textbook: "Sudden and rapid graying of the hair undoubtedly occurs. Even overnight cases are on record. Rapes in young girls have been a common cause—operations, grief due to loss of family, and stark terror have been reported as other causes. . . . Simon describes the curious patient of Duivepart, a healthy male, aged 19 years, who became gray overnight as the result of a terrifying experience in a graveyard. He later had five daughters who were all victims of a precocious canities [graying of the hair]."

Here Dr. McCarthy piles Pelion upon Ossa: not only does he have hair turning gray overnight as the result of a terrifying experience—but he describes the transmission of acquired characteristics to the five offspring. It's enough to make a person's hair turn white.

Graying of the hair, like baldness, is determined by heredity. The age at which a person will become gray, or start getting gray, is determined by certain time genes inherited from one's parents. Almost always it is found that graying begins and is completed in an individual at about the same age in which it occurred in one parent or the other.

Perhaps the best bon mot on the subject is from *The Importance of Being Earnest* when Algernon Moncrieff says to Lady Bracknell, "I hear that her hair has turned quite gold from grief."

SQUARE-JAWED HE-MAN; WEAK-CHINNED SISSY?

It's as dangerous to judge a man by his chin as it is to judge a book by its cover. One naturally associates the face which ends in a great square jaw with power, toughness, strength—especially if there is a five-o'clock shadow, or even a beard, on it. One thinks of the bulldog, certain fearful-looking denizens of the deep, and other prognathous monsters, and one never stops to imagine that there goes a glass jaw which a well-placed right, timed accurately from the shoulder, would probably cause to fold up like a tent. Likewise the person with a chin scarcely visible to the naked eye is deemed a weak character.

An afternoon in the galleries showing portraits of famous persons—or a few hours in the newspaper morgue—is quite enough to set this error straight, for what said Duncan? "There's no art to read the mind's construction in the face." The Spanish Hapsburgs represent a long line of royalty most of whose members were endowed with overdeveloped lower jaws of great "strength," yet who were personally and individually conspicuously weak characters.

"Who do you think you are—Samson?" a heckler asked Cyrano.

"Precisely," answered our Gascon. "Will you kindly lend me your jawbone?"

Always Singe the Hair After a Haircut?

If you happen to enjoy the smell of burning hair, by all means urge the barber to singe after cutting. The only benefit, however, will be your delight in the scent. But there's no reason you should deny yourself this aroma if you go for it.

The idea may be on the wane these days, but not long ago it was generally "known" that hair bleeds when it is cut; that the "vital fluid" must be kept in, and the way to do it is to cauterize the ends.

In a word, No. Hair has no fluid in it, vital or lethal. It does not bleed. But it sure does smell when you burn it.

We Are Physically Weaker Than Our Ancestors?

"When our houses were of willow," proclaimed the old saw, "then were our men of oak. But now that our houses are of oak, our men are become of willow." In other words, everybody is living a soft life and losing his toughness as a result. The younger generation has been going to the dogs for so many centuries that it is shocking. When soccer was introduced into England, the old-timers were disgusted: here were tall youths kicking a ball around in the meadow by the river when they should be learning how to cut each other to pieces with swords. Ah, me. The lost generation. Effete, weaklings all.

Probably the whispering campaign about how much tougher our ancestors were came from retired generals and pensioned soldiers who, like Menelaus grown old, "waxed garrulous and sacked a hundred Troys twixt noon and supper," as Rupert Brooke put it. Any old-time truck driver will regale his listeners with how rugged the work was before power brakes and power steering; and if you know some Dartmouth graduate of the years 1900-1915, get him to tell you how nobody shaved between the Harvard game and Christmas. Or just let him ramble on at will. He'll get to it.

Actually, the researches of Franz Boas, Gordon T. Bowles, and a score of others have established beyond question that today's generation is stronger and healthier on the average than their grandparents. Any college that keeps records of parents and children enrolled there can document the fact that the Class of 1966 was taller and heavier than the Class of 1926. The same is true in Europe, in the industrialized lands: military records in The Netherlands indicate that the average size of recruits increased five inches between 1850 and 1907.

Science Service reported from Washington in 1960 that "Young men and women in the United States today average about two inches taller than those 60 years ago, a study of the heights and weights of adults over the past 100 years shows.

"Miss Millicent L. Hathaway and Miss Elsie D. Foard of the Department of Agriculture's Research Service report that the younger generation in college in recent years has averaged about an inch taller than their parents. The sons weighed five to ten pounds more; the daughters, two to five pounds more."

When Gertrude Ederle swam the English Channel all the front pages told about it; but the other day when someone made the round trip—both ways without stopping—we can't even remember who it was. . . .

The Solitary Man Cannot Survive in the Jungle?

We have been told so often that we do not have ripping-talon claws, rending-tusk fangs, or some other deadly attribute of the great cats in the jungle that most of us believe the folk myth that unless man had joined up in cooperation with a bunch of others of his species or made use of killing-tools he would never have survived the jungle. Our species is much tougher and hardier than it gets credit for. The human heart will outlast almost any mechanical pump ever made in terms of work output; and physically man is one of the largest and strongest of all earth's mammals. In the natural state there were not, probably, half a dozen of the many living things that he had any reason to fear, despite the fact that he inherited no protective armor of either fur or shell.

If you don't want to accept the story of Samson and the lion, you won't deny the written records of Carl Akeley, the explorer, and of Stewart Edward White, the writer, who were each attacked by a leopard and killed the attacker with their bare hands. True, they did not *seek* the encounter. But they won it.

EARLY SHAVING ENCOURAGES BEARD GROWTH?

Many a chin, and many a manly chest, too, has been made to bleed untimely from razor nicks occurring when a valiant youth has sought to hasten the growth of his hirsute attestation to manhood. Probably in these days they're using electric shavers. But *they* won't help any more than the blades did. No amount of scraping the skin will increase the number or the activity of the hair follicles. The time of the appearance—and disappearance—of hair in the male is a matter of heredity.

Cognate with the early-shaving myth is the notion, once very current, that a balding man should shave his beard closely every day so that no nourishment should be diverted from the pate. Of course it doesn't make the slightest difference.

We don't want to spoil anybody's fun—or anybody's business either—but it seems that no evidence is available that any treatment or application is going to grow hair where the inheritance of the genes directs otherwise. Dr. Mildred Trotter took the time to explode three methods supposedly encouraging hair growth: the application of petroleum; shaving; and sunburn. All three had been supported by popular belief as being effective. Not one of them did a single thing to help, she reported.

BOTH JAWS MOVE WHEN YOU ARE EATING OR TALKING?

Many famous men have asserted with absolute conviction that both jaws move. But stop and think for a minute. Let's see you move your upper jaw without moving the whole head. You can't do it. Up or down or sideways—if that upper jaw moves, so does all the rest of your skull. The upper jaw, obviously, is fixed; it is stationary. You can hold your head perfectly still and move your *lower* jaw to your heart's content, however.

Of course the upper *lip* moves, and maybe that is what deceives so many people. Try the question on a few friends—you'll be surprised how widespread the idea is that both upper and lower jaws do move. And some people won't change their minds about it either.

A Summer Cold Is More Tenacious Than a Winter Cold?

It is not hard to understand why some people are completely adamant on this subject: absolute granite, they are. To your joyful intonation to June, "Then, if ever, come perfect days. . . . Every clod feels a stir of might," meaning yourself, these people answer bitterly, "If she be not so for me, what care I how fair she be?" meaning June. But the difference in your viewpoints has really nothing at all to do with the colds you both get in the summer, from time to time. Appearances indicate that your cold clears up in two weeks and theirs takes a month, which is reason enough to say, "It lasts forever with me."

In full truth, no. While the viruses causing summer and winter colds may differ somewhat, there is no evidence that there is any difference in the duration of the colds they induce. They have the same incubation period and run the same course, December or June.

But in the summer there are many other airborne irritants to which some people are allergic. We know a gentleman with a nose of prodigal proportions at whose feet Cyrano could have sat weeping in jealous rage. This nasal appendage captures the very first whiff of opening buds before the rest of us feel that spring is even around the corner. It then enters a state of supreme indignation, reddens, fills with liquids of one sort or another, and keeps its poor master in a continual state of sniffing driers or spraying medicaments. This man *knows* that he always catches a cold in

May and that it stays until July, and it would be physically hazardous to tell him that a summer cold is no worse than a winter cold. So it just depends on what one means by "A cold in the head."

Men Have Mechanical Aptitudes Not Given to Women?

Rosie the Riveter is too recent an addition to our society for us to be able to say for certain whether the day will come in this country when men will regard manual dexterity with tools as one of the more engaging traits of femininity. Dexterity with a needle or a loom, and especially with a stove, has always been lauded as a desirable characteristic on the part of the distaff side; and suspicion—perhaps jealousy—has attended the woman who outdid the men in the use of the tools of industry and factory, although employers now know that where precision and delicacy of handling are concerned women are not only equal to men but superior.

No, the hoary error about women's alleged mechanical ineptitude is one which has been encouraged—let's face it—by the women themselves. They want to exhibit those traits which are most pleasing to the male's idea of what a woman should be. And who wants to marry a female grease monkey? For that matter, who wants a woman around the house who is more dextrous in driving a nail or repairing a faucet than the master himself?

For Frostbite: Rub It with Snow?

Perhaps it is some association with the idea of a "blanket" of snow or of snow acting as a protection against the cold and the wind for the small creatures below that is responsible for the idiotic idea that rubbing the skin with snow is a good thing for frostbite. One of the men who knew the most about life in the killing cold climates, a man who lived off the land himself with no contact with the outside world for two years (and who was thereupon given up as lost forever), was Vilhjalmur Stefansson; and he himself said, in *My Life with the Eskimo* (p. 76), that "few things could be more absurd" than the snow treatment for frostbite. He pointed out that ignorant explorers, trustful of the old prescription of the folk, had frozen the whole surfaces of their faces by massaging them with snow when it was 40° below or more. "All you have to do," he said, "is to take your warm hand out of your mitten and press it on the frozen spot for a moment until the whiteness and stiffness are gone." Incidentally, it was Stefansson who proved that men could live and be healthy on a diet of nothing but meat for a considerable length of time. His party was given up for lost because the experts knew that he must have used up his civilized supplies long since and they *thought* they knew that our species could not survive on a meat diet. But the valiant son of Icelandic parents came back to give gentle but living reproof to that theory—and he was healthy and active until his death at the age of eighty-five, and had a never-failing sense of humor, which is another miracle.

Never Stop Moving if You're Lost in a Blizzard?

Stefansson also gave the lie to that companion piece of non-sense that asserts that it is fatal to sit down or sleep if one is lost in a blizzard, because there is no waking from such a sleep. One must continue stumbling along somehow, at all costs, according to this venerable lunacy and fight off sleep by sheer will power if necessary.

This particular illusion, says Stefansson, has caused dozens of arctic deaths; explorers, believing the old saw, have wandered on and on until they were utterly exhausted and their powers of resistance were reduced. Then they have collapsed and frozen to death, unable to twitch a finger in self-protection. But the experienced Eskimo knows better: the important thing to do is to conserve one's strength, not waste it in wild plunging. One should sit in the most sheltered spot available with one's back to the wind and get as much sleep as possible.

For Burns: Apply Heat to the Affected Part?

This is the counterpart of the frostbite-snow myth. The homeo-pathic domestic remedy of curing similars with similars is probably a fairly recent invention as the history of man goes. Prehistoric man must have had many opportunities for burning himself. It is very unlikely that he ever thought of doing anything so foolish as to apply heat to the affected part. He probably did what any child would think of doing: get to the nearest cold water and keep in it whatever part of one's anatomy has been burned. Try it the next time you burn your finger and judge for yourself.

The cure for heat exhaustion is not exposure to the sun, but a cold bath or shower or hosing down.

Some Infectious Diseases Are Inherited?

When a person is sick, it always seems to be emotionally gratifying to be able to spot the source of the illness. If one can say, "I caught this cold right straight from Uncle Frank," that somehow relieves the sufferer of any responsibility for picking up the cold on his own; one is now suffering unjustly and obviously deserves a great deal of sympathy. Maybe this goes deep into the abysm of time when an illness was proof of one's being punished by an evil spirit. At any rate, it is a common belief that certain infectious diseases are inherited, and let us say immediately that this is fatuous: no infectious disease can be inherited.

On the heels of this statement should come the acknowledgment that an unborn child can contract some diseases—syphilis especially—in the womb and is therefore born with it; but the disease was not an inheritance in the sense that it was contained in the genes derived from his parents. He picked it up at one stage of his own life, although of course without any fault of his own.

A *weakness* can be inherited which makes one liable to develop a certain disease, so that the person is predisposed to fall a victim to it if the conditions are right, where a normal person would not.

It used to be an accepted "fact" that tuberculosis was more frequently inherited than any other disease; but it is known now that this is not the truth. That t.b. runs through some families is now believed to be because a predisposition to it was inherited, an infection occurred, and the child was subject to the same environment in which the parents lived when they were afflicted.

A Pinprick Is More Dangerous Than a Needle Prick?

It seems to be a very widespread notion that if one needed a drop of blood for a test or something it would be much safer to use a needle than a pin. One can remember from youth some howling non sequitur to the effect that since a needle was steel and a pin was copper or some baser metal or alloy, obviously the steel was safer. Why? One never asked. Steel: fine. Steel is somehow honorable. Excalibur, forged by fairies in Avalon, was finest steel. . . . Well, it makes for lovely romance, but extremely poor medicine. Like the legend of the rusty nail or the rusty pin being more dangerous than the clean one, it's pure nonsense. Of course if the pin has been lying around the house and the needle has been in a closed case, there's less chance of the needle's point being the resting place of bacteria; but it will be the bacteria, not the metal, that will cause an infection if there is one. The rust on a piece of steel or iron is harmless oxide of iron—ferrous or ferric, we never could get that part straight—and won't cause infection. But here again one has to remember that a rusty nail is probably also a dirty nail, and may be a more cheerful home for bacteria than a shiny new one. After all, the bacteria like *their* comfort, too.

If You're Hungry a Lot—Tapeworm?

More or less universal is the understanding that a tapeworm eats so much of its victim's food that normal servings are not enough for the host and he is liable to be perpetually hungry. Fact is, increased appetite without marked increase of weight is more likely to be an indication of some disturbance in metabolism rather than the presence of a tapeworm. In reality, a tapeworm eats very little, so little that the amount is scarcely noticeable. The parasite, indeed, gives hardly any sign at all that he is present.

It used to be thought that if you ground your teeth at night you had intestinal worms, but there's nothing in that either.

THOMAS MEEHAN

Il Talento Mysterioso

It was, I recall, on a torpid New York evening in the late summer of 1965, a few years ago now, that I had the first inkling that
I possess an almost supernatural gift for translating foreign languages into English. My wife and I, along with a couple named
Bert and Ella Amberstone, had been to the Greenwich Theatre
to see a revival of Antonioni's "L'Avventura," a film we'd all
somehow missed on its first trip around, and afterward, when we
adjourned to a West Eleventh Street restaurant called Gene's,
there was about twenty minutes of dead silence, during which
none of the four of us—fiddling with saltcellars, tapping our fingers on the tabletop, gazing up at the ceiling—could think of a
damned thing to say about the movie. Finally, in desperation, I
broke the ice. "'L'Avventura,'" I said, nervously clearing my
throat. "I suppose you'd translate that as 'The Adventure.'"

Ella Amberstone gazed at me in amazement. "Do you know
Italian?" she asked, a hint of wonder in her voice.

"Actually, no," I admitted. "I don't know a word of Italian."

"Well, I think that's in*cred*ible," she said. "Your translation is
inspired, getting over the literal meaning perfectly while at the
same time capturing all of the subtler nuances in the title."

203

"Really?" I said, blushing, unable to suppress a pleased grin. Ella, as I only then remembered, had lived in Florence for three years and spoke Italian fluently.

"Come on—you've studied Italian," she said, winking at her husband. Apparently, she thought that I was kidding her.

"Uh-uh, I swear," I said, my grin getting even broader. "It just sort of came to me. 'The Adventure.' "

At first, I assumed that my flawless translation of "L'Avventura" had been a fluke, but suddenly I found that I had an uncanny ability to translate all sorts of things from Italian into English. Somehow, I seemed to be particularly good on Antonioni titles, and the Amberstones were soon telling all of their friends about my translations of "La Notte" and "L'Eclisse"—"The Night" and "The Eclipse," as I'd rendered them from the colloquial Italian into English.

I next made the staggering discovery that, again without knowing a word of the language, I could also translate from French into English with mysterious ease, and our little circle of acquaintances, led by the Amberstones, was abuzz for days with excited talk of my translations of "La Belle Dame sans Merci" ("The Beautiful Lady Without Mercy") and "Les Enfants du Paradis" ("The Infants of Paradise"). Finally, beginning to frighten even myself, I found that I could also translate German, another language I didn't know, as I next rendered into English both "Der Rosenkavalier" ("The Rosens' Cavalier") and Nietzsche's "Also Sprach Zarathustra" ("Zarathustra Spoke Also").

"But how do you *do* it?" my friends kept asking me.

"I don't know, it just comes to me—maybe something like the way Jeane Dixon can tell the future," I'd answer.

"Well, it's spooky," they'd say. "Damned spooky." And I had to admit that they were right.

One of the things that made all this especially mystifying was the fact that, having gone to a series of extremely progressive schools, including a Montana college where I had majored in madrigal singing, I had never taken a single course in any language—not even English. My wife, Karen, who went to the same college I did, taking her degree in spot welding, was similarly handicapped. Nor had Karen or I had the opportunity to learn a foreign language first hand, for until a couple of months ago, when we spent two weeks in Europe, neither of us had ever been outside of the United States. Our sojourn in Europe, by the way, wasn't a pleasure jaunt but a business trip, my first for a new company I'd recently joined. I managed to sneak Karen along, and we went first to Amsterdam, via Pan Am from New York, and then to Rome.

Despite my proved ability to understand languages that I didn't know, I must admit that we both had the jitters as our plane landed at Amsterdam. After all, if we couldn't speak a word of the language, how were we going to find a hotel, get meals, or even buy a pack of Pall Malls? And how was I to transact my business, which involved trying to sell ski tows to the Dutch government? Thus, as I edgily saw it, we were literally banking everything on my mysterious talent for languages.

"Well, here goes nothing," I said to Karen as, having got through customs, we walked timidly into the main waiting room of the Amsterdam air terminal.

"So what do we do now?" asked Karen nervously.

"Phone for a hotel reservation," I said.

"But how, *how?*" wailed Karen. "We don't know any Dutch."

Suddenly, looking across the waiting room, I spied a row of glass booths, above which there was a sign saying "Telefoon." "Hey, look," I said excitedly to Karen, "*'telefoon.'* That's going to be your 'telephone.' God damn! I can speak Dutch, and I didn't even know it."

And I could. In the phone book I found the number of a hotel some friends had recommended, and then I cleverly watched a small Dutch child use the *telefoon,* and imitated his deft dialling technique. Unfortunately, the people at the hotel spoke to me in English, incredibly having guessed that I was a foreigner, so I didn't have a chance to try out my Dutch on them. But within the hour, after I had made a reservation, we were settled in a suite in the Grand Hotel Krasnapolsky and I was translating Dutch for Karen right and left. "Look," I said to her, pointing to the room-service menu, "for breakfast you can have *koffie*. That's going to be what we in English call 'coffee.' "

"You're amazing," said Karen.

"And this switch here," I went on, "the one marked 'Muziek.' Unless I miss my guess, this ought to give us music." And, sure enough, when I flicked the switch our room was flooded with an aria from "Lucia di Lammermoor" ("Lucy from Lammermoor"). Later, after freshening up, we wandered out to explore Amsterdam, stopping to have a *bier* and a hot dog, *met mosterd* (anyone baffled by words I have left untranslated here can surely get help from the Dutch Embassy in Washington), in a café, to pick up a pack of Pall Mall *cigaretten,* and to buy a *postkaart* to mail back to the magnificent Amberstones. It was a *warme* afternoon, a *Zaterdag,* the beginning of the *weekeinde,* and we had a gay time strolling about. And not once, in our various dealings with Dutch waiters and so forth, was I at a loss for a *woord,* although I was admittedly *helpt* by the fact that everyone in Amsterdam above the age of four seems to be able to speak English with the facility of Sir John Gielgud.

On the way back to the Krasnapolsky, Karen spied a newsstand displaying the international edition of the New York *Times,* but, disdaining the *Times,* I bought a copy of an Amsterdam paper, *De Telegraaf,* or, as I translated it for Karen, *"The Telegraph."* Up in our room, I was soon reading *De Telegraaf* from one end to the other, beginning with a front-page story about *Amerikaanse troepen* in *Zuid-Vietnam,* going on to the sports *nieuws,* and finishing off with my daily *horoscoop* (*"Maakt plannen voor een lange periode van disharmonie"*).

Having been perfectly able to understand Dutch, I felt not a twinge of nervousness when, after five marvellous days in Amsterdam, marred only by my failure to unload a single ski tow, we flew on to Rome. After all, I assured Karen, Italian had been the first language in which my weird gift had evidenced itself. Nonetheless, I couldn't help feeling elated when, as soon as we got off the plane, I was able to usher Karen straight up to a sign saying "Passaporto Controllo."

"Passport control," I whispered to her out of the side of my mouth.

"How do you know?" she asked.

"I just know, that's all," I replied. "It's this spooky gift of mine." And damned if I wasn't right again. "Son of a gun," I said happily to Karen. "It isn't just Antonioni titles—I can speak Italian as well as I can speak Dutch!"

And I could. In fact, within forty-five *minuti* we had checked into the Hotel Excelsior, on the Via Veneto (Veneto Street), and had stepped out to a nearby *ristorante* for dinner, where, as Karen sat with her jaw agape, I calmly ordered an entire meal in Italian: *zuppa di spinaci, bistecca* with creamed *asparagi* and a baked *patata,* a big bottle of *vino,* and, for dessert, a nice piece *frutta*—a *banana.*

"It's unbe*liev*able," Karen said as she peeled her *banana.*

"Yup, it is," I said, leaning grandly back in my chair and lighting an after-dinner *sigaro.*

Later, back at the Excelsior, before going to bed, I casually read through an Italian magazine that I'd picked up at the newsstand downstairs, starting with an article about an amazing new *dieta,* going on to a short story entitled "Un Matrimonio in Crisi," and finishing off with my *oroscopo ("Prepararsi per un periodo negativo").*

The following morning, eager to get on with my business, I rose early. My business in Rome, by the way, involved not ski tows but stained-glass windows, another product of the American company I was representing—a diversified Schenectady outfit that markets a line of ski tows, orthopedic shoes, stained-glass windows, and canoe paddles. In any event, leaping out of bed at 7

A.M., I picked up the *telefono,* called down to room service for a cup of *caffè,* and then headed for the bathroom.

"Ah," I shouted to Karen, "I'm going to take myself a nice icy *caldo* shower!"

"Hey, sweetie, I don't think that '*caldo*' means—" Karen called out to me, but it was too late. With a badly scalded back, I was carted off screaming to *l'ospedale,* where I lay in agony and sullen *silenzio* for the next week.

My *caldo* shower was *un totale disastro,* and so, unhappily, was my business trip, for almost as soon as we returned to New York I was fired. Going over on the plane, I'd sold a pair of orthopedic shoes to a gimpy stewardess, but, as I mentioned, I didn't get rid of any ski tows in Amsterdam, and in Rome I wrote orders for only fourteen dollars' worth of stained-glass windows. Thus, my territory—lower Manhattan, Holland, and Italy—was turned over to another salesman. At the moment, in fact, I'm still out of work, but there ought to be a hot-shot job around somewhere for a go-getter who can translate fluently from Dutch, German, and French, and whose Italian is almost *lettera perfetta.*

HAROLD MEHLING

A Case of Salted Diamonds

IN THE EARLY DAYS OF FEBRUARY, 1872, San Franciscans excitedly received news of the greatest find since the gold dust of '49. Somewhere in the West, someone had stumbled onto an entire mountain of diamonds. Imagine, a whole mountain! No one knew exactly where, but they all knew it was real.

The bearers of this astonishing news looked exactly as they should. John Slack and Philip Arnold were their names, and they were grizzled sourdoughs, with proper mats of beard and the dust of the hill trails on their jeans. Slack was a short, quiet fellow who didn't leave distinct impressions; when a question arose, he let Arnold handle it. Arnold was a long, articulate stringbean with a face full of honest excitement. He was known to have served with Morgan's Raiders during the Civil War and, regardless of sentiments, a guerrilla-fighter was a straight-shooter.

The picturesque pair didn't ride into town shouting their discovery up Market Street, of course. They arrived on a Union Pacific train on the first or second day of the month, Arnold carrying a canvas sack, and Slack beside him dangling a Winchester in the crook of his right arm. After checking into a hotel they went out for a drink, carrying the sack and standing it upright on the floor between them as they bent their elbows. Wherever they went, the sack went with them.

By the middle of February half the barkeeps in San Francisco were conjecturing on the contents of the bag and wondering why it received such close attention. Their interest was also piqued when the sourdoughs conducted all conversation in a whisper. One tavern owner said they seemed frightened, as if they had something too hot to handle, too good to let go.

Either way, the sack was at least heavy, and so Arnold and Slack carried it into the Bank of California and asked to have it deposited in a vault. No sooner had they received a receipt and departed than the inquisitive cashier was in a back room inspecting the contents. He found precious stones—a bagful of rough, uncut diamonds, emeralds, sapphires, and rubies. That was too hot for *him* to handle, so he took his discovery to the bank's president, William C. Ralston.

Bill Ralston was one of San Francisco's big men. He was an investment banker with a free wheeling urge to take a chance. Rarely losing on a venture, he had put together a fortune that elevated him to ranking position among the city's elite. When he peered into the canvas, rubbed the gems in his hands, and heard about the whiskered men, he decided that a big deal was lurking. But being a sharply honed man for all his flamboyancy, he called in an assayer to inspect the stones on a confidential basis. The expert said they were worth about $125,000 and must have been taken out of the ground fairly recently.

Ralston decided that the approach to Arnold, the Civil War veteran, should be made through channels of military camaraderie. So he confided his discovery to an occasional investment partner, George D. Roberts, who had come out of the war as a Union Army general. Roberts immediately suspected that Arnold was the man who had investigated some mining properties for him only two years earlier. At their first meeting the general was delighted; it was the same Arnold.

Roberts seated the sourdoughs around several bottles of good liquor and soon he and Arnold were reliving adventures from Sumter to Appomattox. Although they had fought on opposite sides, new friendships were stronger than old animosities, they agreed.

And so they got down, eventually, to the amazing gem discovery, which caused Arnold to fall back into whispers.

"I thought it would blind us," he said. "We came onto the field and the glittering in the sun was so strong we blinked. Everywhere we turned we saw the stones. Slack here went wild. He dug away with a boot heel and scratched them right out of the ground."

The general's eyes stared glassily. He could almost see the gem field himself. "You fellows are in for a fortune," he said, "if you can just get those stones out of there." He poured another drink and let them ponder his remark.

Arnold and Slack stared uneasily at each other. Then Arnold unburdened himself. "General," he said, "that's what has us stirred up. We've got hold of this thing but we don't know what to do with it. If we start hauling the stones out in sacks, someone'll trace the field. The only way to do it is to tie up the land and bring rigs in to mine it out. But we can't get money for that without selling what we brought out and that would raise suspicion. Now, we don't know who's got that kind of money and some kind of honesty."

The general nodded sympathetically. It was a dilemma he could understand. He talked for fifteen minutes about the sad state of mankind's morals, how things had come to where one human being couldn't trust another. Then he brightened.

"Tell you men what I'll do," he said. "I don't have that kind of money myself, but I'm close to men who do. I can take the problem to them and see if they won't agree to finance a company that would obtain legal title to the field and mine the stones. Naturally, you would be partners in the company. Now, how does that sound?"

Slack seemed just a bit suspicious of the general, but it was clear that Arnold was running the show. He agreed and Slack subsided. But that was as far as the general got. Try as he would, he could not get the pair to tell him where they had made their great discovery.

By the following morning several pressures were working through San Francisco. The cashier who had received the sourdoughs' sack began using his discovery as a conversation piece, and Arnold and Slack found themselves a magnet for the curious and acquisitive. They stopped denying their find, but refused to discuss its location, even vaguely. One evening, however, Arnold seemed to have a drink too many and hinted that the field was west of Omaha and south of Laramie. Despite the fact that this narrowed the field to but half the West, a rumor whistled through town that the cornucopia was in the northeast corner of Arizona, where part of the Navajo Indian reservation is located today. Within a week, fully a thousand men had departed in search of remarkable riches.

Another pressure came from banker Bill Ralston. General Roberts, feeling that he had cut himself in by laying the groundwork, handed the problem of Arnold's and Slack's silence back to Ralston, who had the most persuasive tongue south of the Columbia River. Soon the banker was showing the sourdoughs, in terms they could almost feel, what exploitation of the gem field would mean to them. He spoke of mansions, wine cellars, servants, carriages, women, and position in the community of the rich.

Arnold's hands trembled by the minute as Ralston orated. When he could no longer contain himself he burst out with, "You've got a deal, Mr. Ralston."

"Call me Bill, boys," Ralston said.

Bill got the excited pair to agree to lead two of his associates into the field for a thorough inspection. Arnold insisted on only one caution: Ralston's representatives must be blindfolded until they reached the field.

Two weeks later, when the party returned to San Francisco, the banker's associates were dazed. They didn't know where they'd been, but they had seen more jewels than they could count, and had brought back a bag of them. "Not because we thought anyone would doubt us," they told Ralston, "but because we wanted to be sure ourselves that we hadn't been dreaming."

With Ralston's acquiescence, the news leaked out. It spread through the city as fast as the fire of thirty-odd years later. People accepted the reports without doubt, for the gem find was simply another proof of what they fervently believed: the West, and San Francisco in particular, was fated to become the richest, most powerful area in the burgeoning United States. Without using the exact phrase, civic leaders talked of the city's manifest destiny.

They had ample evidence. The West was still riding a crest of enthusiasm that followed the purchase of Alaska five years earlier. True, some were calling the purchase Seward's Folly, but Westerners knew you couldn't go far wrong for two cents an acre, especially when those acres might contain fabulous fur and mineral riches. And only recently they had enjoyed the golden spike ceremony, the joining of the Central and Union Pacific Railroads that made San Francisco easily accessible to the rest of the growing nation.

As Easterners traveled west for the first time, they found an area that almost constituted a separate nation, a vastness and beauty they had not realized was part of their birthright. Foreigners were awed, too. In 1869 an Englishman had visited Utah and Colorado and returned home to announce that he had discovered several mountains of pure silver. When he offered to share his mountains with people who would invest three million dollars to make molehills out of them, the *Times of London* exposed him as a fraud and he disappeared, but the debacle dampened no enthusiasm for the American West.

That was the prevailing spirit of confidence which led San Franciscans to place wholehearted faith in Arnold's and Slack's Western gem field. Twenty-five bold citizens gave banker Ralston $80,000 apiece to get in on the ground floor of the new San Francisco and New York Mining and Commercial Company. Then

Baron Ferdinand Rothschild of London and Paris came in and so did a couple of New Yorkers named Horace Greeley and Charles Tiffany. Greeley had left the New York *Tribune* but was still a formidable name, and Tiffany was the founder of the noted Fifth Avenue jewelry firm.

With over $2,000,000 in capital at his disposal, Bill Ralston continued to combine caution with a keen sense of public relations. He told Arnold and Slack he wanted to submit their bag of gems to Tiffany, the most noted American authority on precious stones. The sourdoughs quickly agreed, which set the scene for a publicity-laden meeting at Tiffany's offices in New York. Present, in addition to the luminaries mentioned, was Abe Lincoln's unsuccessful presidential opponent, General George B. McClellan, one of the directors of the firm.

When everyone was seated and the reporters had been briefed, Ralston approached a large table at which Tiffany sat. He carried a sack of stones which, with some effort, he lifted and upended. The gems spilled into a large heap before Tiffany, and the audience gasped. The jeweler fingered a few and rubbed them. He held them up to the light and finally subjected them to searching inspection through a jeweler's glass.

"These are precious stones of enormous value," he said.

"How much value?" Bill Ralston asked.

"I will have to submit them to my lapidaries for an exact appraisal," Tiffany replied. The fact was that the jeweler knew next to nothing about uncut diamonds.

For forty-eight hours the newspapers kept the story boiling, and then came the verdict. When cut, the gems would be worth $150,000. Ralston, who had brought only a tenth of the stones from his vaults, hurried down to Washington to conduct some further business. He looked up Senator Ben Butler and hired him as a legal consultant. Butler, a Westerner whom the Senate looked to in matters of mining and minerals, agreed that he would be invaluable in getting Congress to legalize the firm's claim to the gem field.

It might seem that Bill Ralston had subjected the sourdoughs' veracity to the ultimate test. But no. An insatiable pursuer of peace of mind, he suggested that, as a last condition, the field be examined by a consulting engineer whose reputation was without a blemish. When Arnold and Slack again agreed, Ralston retained Henry Janin, an engineer so conservative in appraisals that he was said to have approved five hundred mines in which clients later prospered, none in which they lost money. Janin received his price: $2,500, all his expenses, and the right to buy shares in the firm at a low price.

Again Arnold and Slack interrupted the gracious life they were enjoying in San Francisco on a cash advance of $100,000 made by Ralston, and conducted a blindfolded expedition to their Shangri-la. But this time Arnold laid the groundwork for his exit by first protesting bitterly that he and Slack were being put to immense trouble. When they returned to San Francisco this time, Janin added his expert opinion to the others that had confirmed the find. Soon Ralston was turning down offers of as much as $200,000, plus twenty percent royalties, for one-acre claims near the still undisclosed site. One hundred thousand shares of stock in the mining company were issued and distributed among the original investors; this was too good a thing to let the grubby public share.

But Ralston found that Arnold's patience had been too sorely tried, and Slack's emotions lavishly followed suit. Arnold said that while the big money men had set themselves up to earn a fortune, he and Slack had been continually stalled. He wanted out, and would settle for $550,000. Ralston happily paid it in cash and said a fond farewell to the sourdoughs, who divulged the location of the gem field and immediately left town—Slack to disappear forever and Arnold to return to his birthplace in northern Kentucky, where he was triumphantly received as a true and successful son of the South.

Knowing nothing of these startling developments, Clarence King, a young geologist, arrived in San Francisco in September,

1872, after having spent the better part of five years studying the mineral lands of the West. King was a product of Yale, and at thirty, a scientist respected for both theoretical and practical knowledge. One of his most recent tasks had been to survey the Fortieth Parallel for the government, which was why he received the gem field news with considerable surprise. He had reported that the geological makeup of Nevada, Utah, Colorado, and Wyoming showed no possibility of precious stone formations. He doubted that Arizona would be an exception.

King found Janin, whom he knew, and got the entire story. The engineer, still high with excitement, said he and Arnold had traveled thirty-six hours on the Union Pacific before debarking in western Wyoming.

"Then he blindfolded me," Janin related, "and put me on a horse. We rode for two days with the sun in our faces a lot of the time. When we got there and Arnold took my blindfold off, I saw the most beautiful view I've ever come across. We were high, I figure about 7,000 feet, and standing on a mesa that was mostly desert, but right near us was a conical mountain with a flat top. That was the field. In ten minutes I dug out maybe $10,000 worth of stones. They were everywhere, in gulches, between rocks and in shallow holes. Clarence, you ought to get in on this yourself. I know you said there wouldn't be diamonds around the Fortieth Parallel, but swallow your pride and take a look yourself. Anybody can make a mistake, Clarence."

King would swallow neither his pride nor Janin's story. Instead, he reviewed the method by which the engineer had been taken to the gem field. Arizona was out of the question, he decided, because two day's ride from Wyoming would only get a man halfway. Then he recalled that Janin had said the sun was in his face "a lot of the time." To the suspicious King, that sounded as if the engineer had been sandbagged. He had been led back and forth over the same general area for a couple of days. So King went back over his Rocky Mountain field notes and found a description that matched Janin's. He was not precise in his recollection of the mountain, but he knew it was somewhere in eastern Utah, in the Uinta Mountain foothills, just south of the Wyoming line.

Taking the Central Pacific line into Wyoming, he located an old prospector who had cared for his pack horses during geological expeditions. Together they scoured the Uinta foothills country until they reached a lofty elevation. There they found the conical mountain. It was no more than twenty-five miles south of the Central Pacific tracks. King grinned as he recalled that when Janin told Arnold he thought he heard a train whistle, the Kentuckian said, "You're suffering from gem fever, man! That was an Indian yell."

While King bedded down for the night, his helper, intrigued by the story of the gems, began scratching in the sandy soil. Ten minutes later he brought King a large, rough diamond. He had found it in a hole that, on inspection, looked as if it had been made by a miner's steel tool. Then, as King was dropping off to sleep, the old prospector whooped.

"Mr. King," he shouted, "this is the greatest gem field in the world. It even produces cut diamonds!"

Sure enough, he held a stone whose face had felt the knife of a lapidary.

In the morning King went to work. He found sapphires, rubies, garnets, and emeralds, a disparate collection that nature could not possibly produce in one area. He found them stuck between rocks that showed tool marks under a magnifying glass; rocks without scratches yielded no stones. He even found a diamond in the crook of a tree branch. The field ran over a quarter-mile area and ended as abruptly as it started. It had obviously been salted, loaded with stones that nature had manufactured in various parts of the world, but never in the American West.

King and the prospector rode out to the railroad station, where the geologist wired Ralston that he had been duped. The banker refused to believe it until he established King's identity. Then he wired back that he and Janin were coming out to Wyoming and wanted King to lead them into the land of the deflated bauble. King obliged, and the end of the saga came quickly.

The San Francisco and New York Mining and Commercial Company retreated into obscurity, and embarrassed explanations were issued to a bewildered public: Ralston and General Roberts had been taken in by greed fed on rumor; Tiffany was totally unfamiliar with raw diamonds, as were his lapidaries, and had been psychologically prepared to feel that the stones were genuine; Janin, having been called in only after eminent figures had endorsed the field, was also ready to believe anything.

The deluded San Franciscans finally pieced together the story of how they had been fleeced. Arnold and Slack had gone to Europe in 1871 and visited several Amsterdam diamond merchants. All they ever showed interest in were low-grade diamonds, stones that had been rejected because of flaws or poor coloration. The merchants called the pair "the dumb Americans." Then they suddenly departed for London, where they stimulated additional disrespect for American intelligence. Altogether, they spent almost $50,000 for the biggest mess of low quality, rough diamonds ever collected by anybody. As a bonus of inadvertence, they also got the polished diamond that Clarence King's helper came onto after they had returned to America and salted the Uinta foothill.

Banker Ralston knew that since Kentucky was still not gently disposed toward Northerners and particularly Northerners who called a Southerner a swindler, he would never get $650,000 worth of satisfaction out of Arnold on his home ground.

But one investor, whose bitterness was proportionate to the amount of greed that had led him to buy out other investors, traveled down to Kentucky and found Arnold in Elizabethtown, operating as a highly respected banker. He initiated such a pester of legal actions that Arnold finally bought immunity from prosecution by returning $150,000. The rest he used to finance his bank's expansion, an action that so vexed the other bank in town that its owner strolled up to Arnold one day and shot him dead.

The West was still without native-born diamonds, but it was not lacking in excitement. Two years after the exposure of the great diamond fraud, Bill Ralston's Bank of California failed under the weight of his wild speculations. Ralston, short by $5,000,000, was found floating in San Francisco Bay. The ghost who stalks abandoned old mines—even nonexistent gem fields—had claimed its final victim.

RUSSELL MALONEY

Inflexible Logic

WHEN THE SIX CHIMPANZEES came into his life, Mr. Bainbridge was
thirty-eight years old. He was a bachelor and lived comfortably in
a remote part of Connecticut, in a large old house with a carriage
drive, a conservatory, a tennis court, and a well-selected library.
His income was derived from impeccably situated real estate in
New York City, and he spent it soberly, in a manner which could
give offence to nobody. Once a year, late in April, his tennis court
was resurfaced, and after that anybody in the neighborhood was
welcome to use it; his monthly statement from Brentano's seldom
ran below seventy-five dollars; every third year, in November, he
turned in his old Cadillac coupé for a new one; he ordered his
cigars, which were mild and rather moderately priced, in ship-
ments of one thousand; because of the international situation he
had cancelled arrangements to travel abroad, and after due
thought had decided to spend his travelling allowance on wines,
which seemed likely to get scarcer and more expensive if the war
lasted. On the whole, Mr. Bainbridge's life was deliberately, and
not too unsuccessfully, modelled after that of an English country
gentleman of the late eighteenth century, a gentleman interested

in the arts and in the expansion of science, and so sure of himself that he didn't care if some people thought him eccentric.

Mr. Bainbridge had many friends in New York, and he spent several days of the month in the city, staying at his club and looking around. Sometimes he called up a girl and took her out to a theatre and a night club. Sometimes he and a couple of classmates got a little tight and went to a prizefight. Mr. Bainbridge also looked in now and then at some of the conservative art galleries, and liked occasionally to go to a concert. And he liked cocktail parties, too, because of the fine footling conversation and the extraordinary number of pretty girls who had nothing else to do with the rest of their evening. It was at a New York cocktail party, however, that Mr. Bainbridge kept his preliminary appointment with doom. At one of the parties given by Hobie Packard, the stockbroker, he learned about the theory of the six chimpanzees.

It was almost six-forty. The people who had intended to have one drink and go had already gone, and the people who intended to stay were fortifying themselves with slightly dried canapés and talking animatedly. A group of stage and radio people had coagulated in one corner, near Packard's Capehart, and were wrangling about various methods of cheating the Collector of Internal Revenue. In another corner was a group of stockbrokers, talking about the greatest stockbroker of them all, Gauguin. Little Marcia Lupton was sitting with a young man, saying earnestly, "Do you really want to know what my greatest ambition is? I want to be myself," and Mr. Bainbridge smiled gently, thinking of the time Marcia had said that to him. Then he heard the voice of Bernard Weiss, the critic, saying, "Of course he wrote one good novel. It's not surprising. After all, we know that if six chimpanzees were set to work pounding six typewriters at random, they would, in a million years, write all the books in the British Museum."

Mr. Bainbridge drifted over to Weiss and was introduced to Weiss's companion, a Mr. Noble. "What's this about a million chimpanzees, Weiss?" he asked.

"Six chimpanzees," Mr. Weiss said. "It's an old cliché of the mathematicians. I thought everybody was told about it in school. Law of averages, you know, or maybe it's permutation and combination. The six chimps, just pounding away at the typewriter keys, would be bound to copy out all the books ever written by man. There are only so many possible combinations of letters and numerals, and they'd produce all of them—see? Of course they'd also turn out a mountain of gibberish, but they'd work the books in, too. All the books in the British Museum."

Mr. Bainbridge was delighted; this was the sort of talk he liked to hear when he came to New York. "Well, but look here," he said, just to keep up his part in the foolish conversation, "what if one of the chimpanzees finally did duplicate a book, right down to the last period, but left that off? Would that count?"

"I suppose not. Probably the chimpanzee would get around to doing the book again, and put the period in."

"What nonsense!" Mr. Noble cried.

"It may be nonsense, but Sir James Jeans believes it," Mr. Weiss said, huffily. "Jeans or Lancelot Hogben. I know I ran across it quite recently."

Mr. Bainbridge was impressed. He read quite a bit of popular science, and both Jeans and Hogben were in his library. "Is that so?" he murmured, no longer feeling frivolous. "Wonder if it has ever actually been tried? I mean, has anybody ever put six chimpanzees in a room with six typewriters and a lot of paper?"

Mr. Weiss glanced at Mr. Bainbridge's empty cocktail glass and said drily, "Probably not."

Nine weeks later, on a winter evening, Mr. Bainbridge was sitting in his study with his friend James Mallard, an assistant professor of mathematics at New Haven. He was plainly nervous as he poured himself a drink and said, "Mallard, I've asked you to come here—Brandy? Cigar?—for a particular reason. You remember that I wrote you some time ago, asking your opinion of . . . of a certain mathematical hypothesis or supposition."

"Yes," Professor Mallard said, briskly. "I remember perfectly. About the six chimpanzees and the British Museum. And I told you it was a perfectly sound popularization of a principle known to every schoolboy who had studied the science of probabilities."

"Precisely," Mr. Bainbridge said. "Well, Mallard, I made up my mind . . . It was not difficult for me, because I have, in spite of that fellow in the White House, been able to give something every year to the Museum of Natural History, and they were naturally glad to oblige me. . . . And after all, the only contribution a lay-man can make to the progress of science is to assist with the drudgery of experiment. . . . In short, I—"

"I suppose you're trying to tell me that you have procured six chimpanzees and set them to work at typewriters in order to see whether they will eventually write all the books in the British Museum. Is that it?"

"Yes, that's it," Mr. Bainbridge said. "What a mind you have, Mallard. Six fine young males, in perfect condition. I had a—I suppose you'd call it a dormitory—built out in back of the stable. The typewriters are in the conservatory. It's light and airy in there, and I moved most of the plants out. Mr. North, the man who owns the circus, very obligingly let me engage one of his best animal men. Really, it was no trouble at all."

Professor Mallard smiled indulgently. "After all, such a thing is not unheard of," he said. "I seem to remember that a man at some university put his graduate students to work flipping coins, to see if heads and tails came up an equal number of times. Of course they did."

Mr. Bainbridge looked at his friend very queerly. "Then you be-lieve that any such principle of the science of probabilities will stand up under an actual test?"

"Certainly."

"You had better see for yourself." Mr. Bainbridge led Professor Mallard downstairs, along a corridor, through a disused music room, and into a large conservatory. The middle of the floor had been cleared of plants and was occupied by a row of six typewriter tables, each one supporting a hooded machine. At the left of each typewriter was a neat stack of yellow copy paper. Empty wastebaskets were under each table. The chairs were the unpadded, spring-backed kind favored by experienced stenographers. A large bunch of ripe bananas was hanging in one corner, and in another stood a Great Bear water-cooler and a rack of Lily cups. Six piles of typescript, each about a foot high, were ranged along the wall on an improvised shelf. Mr. Bainbridge picked up one of the piles, which he could just conveniently lift, and set it on a table before Professor Mallard. "The output to date of Chimpanzee A, known as Bill," he said simply.

" ' "Oliver Twist," by Charles Dickens,' " Professor Mallard read out. He read the first and second pages of the manuscript, then feverishly leafed through to the end. "You mean to tell me," he said, "that this chimpanzee has written—"

"Word for word and comma for comma," said Mr. Bainbridge. "Young, my butler, and I took turns comparing it with the edition I own. Having finished 'Oliver Twist,' Bill is, as you see, starting the sociological works of Vilfredo Pareto, in Italian. At the rate he has been going, it should keep him busy for the rest of the month."

"And all the chimpanzees"—Professor Mallard was pale, and enunciated with difficulty—"they aren't all—"

"Oh, yes, all writing books which I have every reason to believe are in the British Museum. The prose of John Donne, some Anatole France, Conan Doyle, Galen, the collected plays of Somerset Maugham, Marcel Proust, the memoirs of the late Marie of Rumania, and a monograph by a Dr. Wiley on the marsh grasses of Maine and Massachusetts. I can sum it up for you, Mallard, by telling you that since I started this experiment, four weeks and some days ago, none of the chimpanzees has spoiled a single sheet of paper."

Professor Mallard straightened up, passed his handkerchief across his brow, and took a deep breath. "I apologize for my weakness," he said. "It was simply the sudden shock. No, looking at the thing scientifically—and I hope I am at least as capable of that as the next man—there is nothing marvellous about the situation.

These chimpanzees, or a succession of similar teams of chimpanzees, would in a million years write all the books in the British Museum. I told you some time ago that I believed that statement. Why should my belief be altered by the fact that they produced some of the books at the very outset? After all, I should not be very much surprised if I tossed a coin a hundred times and it came up heads every time. I know that if I kept at it long enough, the ratio would reduce itself to an exact fifty per cent. Rest assured, these chimpanzees will begin to compose gibberish quite soon. It is bound to happen. Science tells us so. Meanwhile, I advise you to keep this experiment secret. Uninformed people might create a sensation if they knew."

"I will, indeed," Mr. Bainbridge said. "And I'm very grateful for your rational analysis. It reassures me. And now, before you go, you must hear the new Schnabel records that arrived today."

During the succeeding three months, Professor Mallard got into the habit of telephoning Mr. Bainbridge every Friday afternoon at five-thirty, immediately after leaving his seminar room. The Professor would say, "Well?" and Mr. Bainbridge would reply, "They're still at it, Mallard. Haven't spoiled a sheet of paper yet." If Mr. Bainbridge had to go out on Friday afternoon, he would leave a written message with his butler, who would read it to Professor Mallard: "Mr. Bainbridge says we now have Trevelyan's 'Life of Macaulay,' the Confessions of St. Augustine, 'Vanity Fair,' part of Irving's 'Life of George Washington,' the Book of the Dead, and some speeches delivered in Parliament in opposition to the Corn Laws, sir." Professor Mallard would reply, with a hint of a snarl in his voice, "Tell him to remember what I predicted," and hang up with a clash.

The eleventh Friday that Professor Mallard telephoned, Mr. Bainbridge said, "No change. I have had to store the bulk of the manuscript in the cellar. I would have burned it, except that it probably has some scientific value."

"How dare you talk of scientific value?" The voice from New Haven roared faintly in the receiver. "Scientific value! You—you

—chimpanzee!" There were further inarticulate sputterings, and Mr. Bainbridge hung up with a disturbed expression. "I am afraid Mallard is overtaxing himself," he murmured.

Next day, however, he was pleasantly surprised. He was leafing through a manuscript that had been completed the previous day by Chimpanzee D, Corky. It was the complete diary of Samuel Pepys, and Mr. Bainbridge was chuckling over the naughty passages, which were omitted in his own edition, when Professor Mallard was shown into the room. "I have come to apologize for my outrageous conduct on the telephone yesterday," the Professor said.

"Please don't think of it any more. I know you have many things on your mind," Mr. Bainbridge said. "Would you like a drink?"

"A large whiskey, straight, please," Professor Mallard said. "I got rather cold driving down. No change, I presume?"

"No, none. Chimpanzee F, Dinty, is just finishing John Florio's translation of Montaigne's essays, but there is no other news of interest."

Professor Mallard squared his shoulders and tossed off his drink in one astonishing gulp. "I should like to see them at work," he said. "Would I disturb them, do you think?"

"Not at all. As a matter of fact, I usually look in on them around this time of day. Dinty may have finished his Montaigne by now, and it is always interesting to see them start a new work. I would have thought that they would continue on the same sheet of paper, but they don't, you know. Always a fresh sheet, and the title in capitals."

Professor Mallard, without apology, poured another drink and slugged it down. "Lead on," he said.

It was dusk in the conservatory, and the chimpanzees were typing by the light of student lamps clamped to their desks. The keeper lounged in a corner, eating a banana and reading *Billboard*. "You might as well take an hour or so off," Mr. Bainbridge said. The man left.

Professor Mallard, who had not taken off his overcoat, stood with his hands in his pockets, looking at the busy chimpanzees. "I wonder if you know, Bainbridge, that the science of probabilities takes everything into account," he said, in a queer, tight voice. "It is certainly almost beyond the bounds of credibility that these chimpanzees should write books without a single error, but that abnormality may be corrected by—*these!*" He took his hands from his pockets, and each one held a .38 revolver. "Stand back out of harm's way!" he shouted.

"Mallard! Stop it!" The revolvers barked, first the right hand, then the left, then the right. Two chimpanzees fell, and a third reeled into a corner. Mr. Bainbridge seized his friend's arm and wrested one of the weapons from him.

"Now I am armed, too, Mallard, and I advise you to stop!" he cried. Professor Mallard's answer was to draw a bead on Chimpanzee E and shoot him dead. Mr. Bainbridge made a rush, and Professor Mallard fired at him. Mr. Bainbridge, in his quick death agony, tightened his finger on the trigger of his revolver. It went off, and Professor Mallard went down. On his hands and knees he fired at the two chimpanzees which were still unhurt, and then collapsed.

There was nobody to hear his last words. "The human equation . . . always the enemy of science . . ." he panted. "This time . . . vice versa . . . I, a mere mortal . . . savior of science . . . deserve a Nobel . . ."

When the old butler came running into the conservatory to investigate the noises, his eyes were met by a truly appalling sight. The student lamps were shattered, but a newly risen moon shone in through the conservatory windows on the corpses of the two gentlemen, each clutching a smoking revolver. Five of the chimpanzees were dead. The sixth was Chimpanzee F. His right arm disabled, obviously bleeding to death, he was slumped before his typewriter. Painfully, with his left hand, he took from the machine the completed last page of Florio's Montaigne. Groping for a fresh sheet, he inserted it, and typed with one finger, "UNCLE TOM'S CABIN, by Harriet Beecher Stowe. Chapte . . ." Then he, too, was dead.

ROBERT TRAVER

Little Elmer

ON A FINE AUGUST DAY SOME YEARS AGO, after his hay was in,
a thrifty and prosperous upstate New York farmer by the name of
Frank Palmer drove to town to visit his lawyer. The world had
treated him kindly and he was in good health, but time was passing and he wasn't getting any younger and he wanted to draw his
will. Besides his thriving farm, Farmer Palmer had acquired
considerable livestock and other personal property. He was a
widower; two of his daughters were grown and married; in addition to the hired help, with him on the farm lived two people: his
favorite grandson Elmer Palmer, whose father was dead, and
Elmer's widowed mother, Susan Palmer.

Farmer Palmer carefully explained his situation to his lawyer.
He pointed out that his two daughters were married and comfortably off and so would not need much from him; and that,
aside from seeing that his deceased son's widow Susan should continue to have a roof over her head if anything happened to him,
he wanted his farm and all his property to go ultimately to his little grandson Elmer, the apple of his eye. Could this be done?

It could be done, Farmer Palmer's lawyer gravely assured him;
and in due course Farmer Palmer left the lawyer's office, compla-

228

cently patting the newly signed will in the breast pocket of his uncomfortable "town" clothes. In this document he left two small token legacies to his two married daughters, duly provided for the roof over the head of daughter-in-law Susan, and left the farm and the remainder of his considerable residuary estate to his little grandson Elmer, lock, stock, and barrel.

When he got home from town and gratefully out of his constricting blue serge suit, Farmer Palmer made his first grave mistake, and one that, in the light of developments, probably cost him his life. He took his fourteen-year-old grandson Elmer aside and proudly told him what he had just done. Now the law report from which this story is reconstructed unfortunately does not give us any extended description of little Elmer. But it is evident that he was quite a lad: imaginative, calculating, and relentlessly acquisitive. It also appears that little Elmer's main reaction upon learning of his grandfather's bounty was not one of gratitude for all that the old man proposed to do for him, but rather concern over how quickly grandpa might die so that little Elmer would the sooner take over the farm. Elmer was something of a juvenile monster, you see, a character straight out of Charles Addams.

Farmer Palmer's innocent blunder in telling his grandson of the provisions of his will still might not have cost him his life had he not, once this information was divulged, again got his blue serge suit out of mothballs and begun courting the Widow Bresee. But then again, perhaps dying for love is at least more romantic than merely dying. In any case, not only did Farmer Palmer woo the Widow Bresee, but in the spring, just about a year and a half after the will was drawn, he married her and, not unnaturally, took her home with him to live. Romance, however, had not prevented Farmer Palmer from first craftily entering into an antenuptial contract with the Widow Bresee in which she agreed not to claim any widow's dower rights in his property in the event of his death. The heady vapors of autumnal love had not clouded his canny judgment that much. This shrewd foresight was also quite a break for Elmer because otherwise the old man's will, leaving everything to Elmer, would automatically have been revoked by his marriage. That is the law. And little Elmer seems to have clearly understood all this. Now nearly sixteen, he still remained the apple of his grandpa's eye; despite the abundant allures of the Widow Bresee, Farmer Palmer still wanted little Elmer to have his fine farm and the bulk of his estate when he died. There was only one canker in all this for Elmer: the gnawing chance that dear old grandpa might change his mind about his will. What to do, what to do?

Again it is difficult to reconstruct from the bare legal report the morbid and steamy atmosphere that must have prevailed on the Palmer farm after the Widow Bresee came there to live. "Desire Under the Silo," it might be called. It is even more difficult to imagine that a sixteen-year-old farm boy could have thought of, much less understood, the fairly complex legal implications of the situation. The reported case unfortunately glosses over this tense human drama—but then the reading of law reports is frequently an exercise in austerity, not to say outright frustration. Judges seem to pride themselves so much on their lofty detachment from the realities of human emotion that one is occasionally tempted to shake them.

In any case it is clear from the reported case that at some time during the summer after his remarriage Farmer Palmer made his final and fatal blunder: he remarked in the hearing of his grandson Elmer that he was thinking of revoking his old will and making a new one. This sealed his doom. Acquisitive little Elmer now grew frantic; his worst fears were about to be realized. How could he keep from losing the precious farm? One can see him tossing and scheming at night in his bare farm bedroom. Then one night the answer came. Why hadn't he thought of it before? It was all so obvious. Just suppose that grandpa should suddenly up and die— just happened to, of course. Then he *couldn't* tinker with his darned old will, could he? Or draw any new one? Little Elmer was a youth of action; at dawn he arose and quick got hold of some weed poison. That, alas, was the end of Farmer Palmer.

Unfortunately for little Elmer, some suspicions were aroused over the abrupt agony of Farmer Palmer's departure. An investigation was made—and little Elmer was charged with murder. After a long and dramatic trial during which Elmer unblinkingly maintained his innocence, he was convicted of second-degree murder and sentenced for a term of years to the state reformatory. His extreme youth probably saved him from a much heavier sentence than he got.

Now it might be supposed that this turn of events would have dampened the spirits of little Elmer, that contrition might have set in and that he might now have been satisfied to serve his time and disappear into a grateful fog of obscurity. But not Elmer; he was made of sterner stuff, and contrition was not in him. Even in prison he still schemed to lay his hot little hands on the farm and the rest of the swag for which he had killed his own grandfather. So much did he covet it that when his two aunts—the two married daughters of Farmer Palmer—started a chancery suit to cut off Elmer under the original will, Elmer hired himself not one but two lawyers and squared away to fight the case.

A long hearing on the issue was held in the trial court. Little Elmer was still in prison but in his absence his two resourceful lawyers got in there and valiantly pitched for him. The aunts, through their attorney, maintained that it was neither just nor equitable that Elmer should get his grandfather's estate; that all the world knew he had murdered his grandfather to get immediate possession of the property for himself and to prevent a revocation of the will. Such things simply could not be. Elmer's resourceful lawyers boldly countered that it made no difference whether Elmer had murdered his grandfather. They correctly pointed out that there was no law or statute in New York or anywhere else that prevented a beneficiary under a will who had intentionally plotted the death of his testator from still taking under the will; that Elmer was already serving his rap and that to rule against him would be to impose more punishment than the law specified; and that in any case the statutes on the subject of wills clearly provided certain unmistakable legal ways in which wills might be revoked—and murder was not one of them. "Follow the statute" was their argument in a nutshell, and it proved to be a powerful one.

When the dust of legal combat had settled, the never-say-die Elmer had won his case; the fatally coveted farm was now close to his avid grasp. But the fatherless aunts were by this time thoroughly aroused; they appealed the decision to the Court of Appeals, the highest court in the state. The arguments there were even longer and more bitter than before. Then one day Judge Earl was ready to deliver the opinion of the court. By this time seven years had passed since the fateful will was drawn. Speed has never been a strong point of the creaking machinery of the law and little Elmer had served his time and was now free, pale, and twenty-three. We can only imagine his whirling thoughts as Judge Earl began delivering the opinion of the appellate court. At long last, *this* was it; the old farm was almost in his clutches. . . .

"At the date of the will, and subsequently to the death of the testator, Elmer lived with his grandfather as a member of his family, and at his death was sixteen years old," Judge Earl began. "He knew of the provisions made in his favor in the will, and, that he might prevent his grandfather from revoking such provisions, which he had manifested some intention to do, and to obtain the speedy enjoyment and immediate possession of his property, he willfully murdered him by poisoning him. He now claims the property, and the sole question for our determination is, can he have it?"

No record is left of Elmer's reaction to this ominous opening blast. Judge Earl continued with his opinion: "The defendant says that the testator is dead; that his will was made in due form and has been admitted to probate, and that, therefore, it must have effect according to the letter of the law."

Judge Earl then agreed that if the statutes pertaining to wills must be followed to the letter, as Elmer's lawyers maintained, and as the trial court had already held, this would indeed give property to the murderer of one who makes a will. We may guess that

Elmer's spirits must have here risen a notch. "It was the intention of the lawmakers," the judge continued quietly, "that the donees in a will should have the property given to them." The judge doubtless paused here. One can almost hear him clear his throat. "But it never could have been their intention that a donee who murdered the testator to make the will operative should have any benefit under it. If such a case had been present to their minds, and it had been supposed necessary to make some provision of law to meet it, it cannot be doubted that they would have provided for it."

The good judge then proceeded to review the various ancient maxims of the law, including one of the oldest: "No man shall profit by his own wrong." He quoted Blackstone; he quoted Coke; he drew upon the Code Napoleon; he even quoted Aristotle in Latin. One suspects that had Aristotle been a Roman he would have quoted him in Greek. But the erudite judge was in a bit of a fix. For the plain truth of the matter was that the floundering Judge Earl had very little exact precedent to go on. This strange case was a new kettle of fish. Yet it is clear from his opinion that the judge was revolted to his gizzard by the notion that a murderer could inherit under the will of the man he had murdered; he was struggling to deny him if he could, even if he had to quote from the old cookbook.

He referred next to the earliest doctors, the blood-letting barbers. "There was a statute in Bologna that whoever drew blood in the streets should be severely punished, and yet it was held not to apply to the case of a barber who opened a vein in the street," he said. In his extremity he even poetically invoked God. "It is commanded in the Decalogue that no work shall be done upon the Sabbath, and yet giving the command a rational interpretation founded upon its design the Infallible Judge held that it did not prohibit works of necessity, charity, or benevolence on that day."

Then he got down to cases. It was growing plain that he did not *like* little Elmer. "Here there was no certainty that this murderer would survive the testator, or that the testator would not change his will, and there was no certainty that he would get this property if nature was allowed to take its course. He therefore murdered the testator expressly to vest himself with an estate. Under such circumstances, what law, human or divine, will allow him to take the estate and enjoy the fruits of his crime?"

One can almost see the righteous old judge pause and glare down over his glasses at tense little Elmer. "The will spoke and became operative at the death of the testator," he went on inexorably. "He caused that death, and thus by his crime made it speak and have operation. Shall it speak and operate in his favor? If he had met the testator and taken his property by force, he would have had no title to it. Shall he acquire title by murdering him? If he had gone to the testator's house and by force compelled him, or by fraud or undue influence had induced him to will him his property, the law would not allow him to hold it. But can he give effect and operation to a will by murder and yet take the property? To answer these questions in the affirmative it seems to me would be a reproach to the jurisprudence of our State and an offense against public policy."

One can imagine that it had grown very quiet in the courtroom as the stern old judge pressed on to his conclusion. He now paused to blast the principle of an old North Carolina case cited by Elmer's lawyers, a case where a wife who had connived with her lover to murder her husband was nevertheless held entitled to her dower interest. One can almost hear him snort. "I am unwilling to assent to the doctrine of that case. . . . The widow should not, for the purpose of acquiring property, be permitted to allege a widowhood which she has wickedly and intentionally created." One again sees him pause to glare finally down at pale little Elmer. "The judgment in this case is reversed," he concluded.

The bailiff's hammer would now fall three times; it had the finality of doom. Judge Earl and his colleagues would gather up their rustling black robes and sweep austerely from the tall chamber; a heavy mahogany door would breathe shut. Little Elmer had at last got his comeuppance.

In reaching his decision old Judge Earl may perhaps be forgiven his indignant floundering and occasional flights of voluptuous rhetoric. It was a tough case. After all, when this bomb was dropped in his lap there was little legal precedent on the subject either in New York or elsewhere. You see, Farmer Palmer had made his will in 1880; little Elmer had dispatched him in 1882; and the final court decision itself was handed down 'way back in 1889—many, many years ago. Little Elmer himself would now be a very old man if in fact he has survived all his disappointments and frustrations.

Since then the celebrated New York case of *Riggs v. Palmer* has become a landmark authority on this macabre subject in Anglo-American jurisprudence. A "leading case," as lawyers call it. Rarely does a similar new case come up in which it is not at least cited if not followed. And mostly it is followed. So the blood-letting barber from Bologna lives on and on. Thus did Elmer's talkative grandpa gain a lasting if dubious sort of posthumous fame. Most of us would doubtless prefer to take our little blaze of glory on a quiz program.

This old New York case is a beautiful example of judge-made law—or "judicial legislation," as its harsher critics might put it. The case also probably raised far more complex legal questions than ever it solved. Suppose the testator-killer is acquitted on his later criminal trial? Or the murder is not discovered until after distribution is made to the killer under the will? Or the killer is found insane? And what about those characters who kill their *intestate* or will-less relatives the more rapidly to take under the general laws of descent? Or to *prevent* the making of a will? Or what about life insurance beneficiaries who kill the assured to accelerate the death provisions under a policy? Or to prevent any change in beneficiaries? These are but a few of the macabre possibilities. Can the ancient maxim that the killer cannot profit by his wrong be made to fit all these diverse cases? If so, by what rule of logic or of law? It gives one a mild case of the judicial "bends" just to think of it. This is not to criticize the doctrine of the Riggs case; rather it is to suggest the possible ramifications of its doctrine—that and the capacity of the law to meet and grapple with new situations.

It would be moderately comforting to report that there have been only a few such cases since Grandpa Palmer got his for talking too much. Comforting, yes, but quite erroneous; the dusty lawbooks fairly abound with them. In fact, of late years the murdering of testators the quicker to get their property has reached mildly epidemic proportions. Alas, it seems that those traits of mankind which we call cupidity and greed have not subsided notably since 1882, nor apparently do murderously inclined testamentary beneficiaries, as a class, trouble too much to learn the law before they do their benefactors in. So this grisly seminar will not have been entirely wasted if it dissuades even one itching prospective devisee or legatee from dispatching his maiden aunt in vain. The moral of all this? Don't kill the talkative goose that made the golden will.

JOHN COLLIER

Night, Youth, Paris,
and the Moon

ANNOYED WITH THE WORLD, I took a large studio in Hampstead. Here I resolved to live in utter aloofness, until the world should approach me on its knees, whining its apologies.

The studio was large and high; so was the rent. Fortunately my suit was strongly made, and I had a tireless appetite for herrings. I lived here happily and frugally, pleased with the vast and shadowy room, and with the absurd little musicians' gallery, on which I set my phonograph a-playing. I approved also of the little kitchen, the bathroom, the tiny garden, and even the damp path, sad with evergreens, that led to the street beyond. I saw no one. My mood was that of a small bomb, but one which had no immediate intention of going off.

Although I had no immediate intention of going off, I was unable to resist buying a large trunk, which I saw standing outside a junkshop. I was attracted by its old-fashioned appearance, for I myself hoped to become old-fashioned; by its size, because I am rather small; by its curved lid, for I was always fond of curves; and most of all by a remark on the part of the dealer, who stood picking his nose in the disillusioned doorway of his shop. "A thing like that," said he, "is always useful."

I paid four pounds, and had the large black incubus taken to my studio on a hand-barrow. There I stood it on the little gallery, which, for no reason, ran along the farther end.

This transaction having left me without money, I felt it necessary to sublet my studio. This was a wrench. I telephoned the agents; soon they arranged to bring a client of theirs, one Stewart Musgrave, to inspect my harmless refuge. I agreed, with some reserve. "I propose to absent myself during this inspection. You will find the key in the door. Later you can inform me if my studio is taken."

Later they informed me that my studio was taken. "I will leave," I said, "at four o'clock on Friday. The interloper can come at four-thirty. He will find the key in the door."

Just before four on Friday, I found myself confronted with a problem. On letting one's studio, one locks one's clothes in a press reserved for the purpose. This I did, but was then nude. One has to pack one's trunk. I had a trunk but nothing to put in it. I had bidden the world farewell. Here was my studio—sublet. There was the world. For practical purposes there is very little else anywhere.

The hour struck. I cut the Gordian knot, crossed the Rubicon, burned my boats, opened my trunk, and climbed inside. At four-thirty the interloper arrived. With bated breath I looked out through my little air-and-peep-hole. This was a surprise. I had bargained for a young man of no personal attractions. Stewart Musgrave was a young woman of many.

She had a good look around, pulled out every drawer, peeped into every corner. She bounced herself on the big divan-bed. She even came up onto the little useless gallery, leaned over, recited a line or two of Juliet, and then she approached my modest retreat. "I won't open you," she said. "There might be a body in you." I thought this showed a fine instinct. Her complexion was divine.

There is a great deal of interest in watching a handsome young woman who imagines herself to be alone in a large studio. One never knows what she will do next. Often, when lying there alone, I had not known what I would do next. But then I was alone. She, too, thought she was alone, but I knew better. This gave me a sense of mastery, of power.

On the other hand, I soon loved her to distraction. The hell of it was, I had a shrewd suspicion she did not love me. How could she?

At night, while she slept in an appealing attitude, I crept downstairs, and into the kitchen, where I cleaned up the crockery, her shoes, and some chicken I found in the icebox. "There is," she said to a friend, "a pixie in this studio."

"Leave out some milk," said her friend.

Everything went swimmingly. Nothing could have been more delicate than the unspoken love that grew up between the disillusioned world-weary poet and the beautiful young girl-artist, so fresh, so natural, and so utterly devoid of self-consciousness.

On one occasion, I must admit, I tripped over the corner of a rug. "Who is there?" she cried, waking suddenly from a dream of having her etchings lovingly appraised by a connoisseur.

"A mouse," I telepathed squeakingly, standing very still. She sank into sleep again.

She was more rudely put to sleep some days later. She came in, after being absent most of the evening, accompanied by a man to whom I took an immediate dislike. My instinct never fails me; he had not been in the studio half an hour before he gave her occasion to say, "Pray don't!"

"Yes," said he.

"No," said she.

"I must," said he.

"You mustn't," said she.

"I will," said he.

"You won't," said she.

A vestige of refined feeling would have assured him that there was no possibility of happiness between people so at variance on every point. There should be at least some zone of enthusiastic agreement between every couple; for example, the milk. But whatever his feelings were, they were not refined.

"Why did you bring me here?" said he with a sneer.

"To see my etchings," she replied, biting her lip.

"Well, then—"

"I thought you were a customer."

"I am. A tough customer." With that he struck her on the temple. She fell, mute, inanimate, crumpled.

"Damn it!" said he. "I've killed her. I've done her in. I shall swing. Unless—I escape."

I was forced to admire the cold logic of it. It was, momentarily, the poet's unreasoning prostration before the man of action, the worldling.

Quickly he undressed her. "Gosh!" he said. "What a pity I hit so hard!" He flung her over his shoulder, retaining her legs in his grasp. He bore her up the stairs, into the shadowy balcony. He opened the trunk and thrust her inside. "Here is a fine thing!" I thought. "Here she is, in her condition, alone with me, in my condition. If she knew she was dead she'd be glad." The thought was bitter.

With the dawn he went for a taxi. The driver came in with him; together they bore the trunk to the vehicle waiting outside.

"Strewth, it's heavy!" said the driver. "What yer got in it?"

"Books," said the murderer, with the utmost calm.

If I had thought of saying, *"Paradise Lost,* in two volumes," I should have said it, then and there, and this story would have come to an end. As it was, we were hoisted on to the cab, which drove off in the direction of Victoria.

A jet of cool night air flowed through the air-hole. She, whom I had mourned as dead, inhaled it, and breathed a sigh. Soon she was fully conscious.

"Who are you?" she asked in alarm.

"My name," I said tactfully, "is Emily."

She said, "You are kidding me."

I said, "What is your name?"

She said, "Stewart."

I could not resist the reply, "Then I am Flora MacDonald."

Thus by easy stages I approached the ticklish question of my hitherto hopeless love.

She said, "I would rather die."

I said, "In a sense you have died already. Besides, I am your pixie. Or it may be only a dream, and you could hardly blame yourself for that. Anyway, I expect he will take us to Paris."

"It is true," she said, "that I have always dreamed of a honeymoon in Paris."

"The Paris moon!" I said. "The bookstalls on the *quais*. The little restaurants on the Left Bank!"

"The *Cirque Médrano!*" she cried.

"*L'Opéra!*"

"*Le Louvre! Le Petit Palais!*"

"*Le Bœuf sur le Toit!*"

"Darling," she cried, "if it were not so dark, I would show you my etchings, if I had them with me."

We were in absolute raptures; we heard the ticket being taken for Paris. We were registered; it was next door to being married, and we laughed at the rolling of the vessel. Soon, however, we were carried up an endless flight of stairs.

"*Mon Dieu, mais que c'est lourd!*" gasped the hotel porter. "*Qu'est-ce qu'il y a dans cette malle?*"

"*Des livres,*" said the murderer, with the utmost sangfroid.

"*Paradis Retrouvé, édition, complète,*" I whispered, and was rewarded with a kiss.

Alone, as he thought, with his lifeless victim, the murderer sneered. "H'ya keeping?" said he coarsely, as he approached the trunk.

He lifted the lid a little, and thrust his head within. A rim ran round inside: while yet he blinked, we seized it, and brought the lid down with a crash.

"*La guillotine?*" I said cuttingly.

"La Defarge!" observed my adored one, knitting her brows.

"Vive la France!"

We stepped out; we put him inside. I retained his clothes. With a sheet from the bed, the bell rope, and a strip of carpet from before the washstand, she made a fetching Arab lass. Together we slipped out into the street.

Night! Youth! Paris! And the moon!

ELISABETH MANN BORGESE

Elephant Intelligence

THE WILD ELEPHANTS in the Munnar district of Kerala State, South India, are several hundreds in number. They move in small herds, comprising seven to nine animals, although occasionally larger herds, of twenty animals, have been sighted. Stolid yet restless creatures, always in search of greener pastures, juicier bamboo, spicier cardamom, or richer salt licks, they wander as far as sixty miles in a night, taking it easy by day in the shade of a big jack-fruit tree, hidden by tall jungle grass.

At night these elephants are uneasy visitors to the plantations. They come on dark nights moving out of the jungle and into the road, silent like gigantic shadows. On moonlit nights they play strange games on the slopes in the backyards of Munnar. Two elephants who descended on Arividak Estate (whose guests we were), under a full moon, strode onto the lawn, and engaged in a sort of round dance: trunk to trunk, they would describe a full circle with their hind legs, round and round, for several minutes. Then they walked back into the jungle.

Another kind of elephant game has been observed, time and again, on the steep slopes bounding the valley. Between the tea groves and the rising blue eucalyptus plantations, which give the valley a park-like appearance under the moonlight, the animals, young ones as well as older, would appear on the crest, get down on their hindquarters and amuse themselves by sliding down the slopes, like giant otters—not without causing considerable damage to the plantation they chose to visit.

Many a building in the valley has been brought down during the nightly calls of these living bulldozers. *"Aani,"* the tribesmen would say, with an almost religious respect, pointing to the ruins of a white temple. *Aani* is the Tamil word for "elephant." There was lime in the mortar, the English planter said. They break down walls for a lick of lime.

White walls, white temples are demolished more frequently than others. Elephants seem to have a predilection, or maybe a pet hatred, for white.

Near the valley, the forest officer recently laid out a new road through the jungle. The route was marked with white stones, every hundred yards. There they stood, neat and white, a rhythmically recurrent scandal to elephant feelings. The elephants must have met in council. They must have voted to do something radical, something systematic, about the affront. Whether or not this was the case, the fact remains that after the first full moon no white stone was left standing. The elephants had uprooted and undone them all, each one of the them, from the beginning to the end of the new jungle road.

The forest officer was a clever strategist, however, not easily discouraged. He replaced the stones, but had them painted dark green. The elephants accepted the compromise. No stone has been turned over since then.

Some of the elephant memories in the valley are more tragic, if not less mysterious.

Three years ago a woman was cutting jungle grass on a tea plantation near Munnar. The grass was tall, more than a man's height and the woman groped her way, moving in the direction of the mountains. At one point her curved jungle knife hit something harder than grass. She withdrew it, horrified at seeing it blood-stained. The elephant was as shocked as his involuntary aggressor. He wound his trunk around the woman, picked her up, raised her high above the ground, swung her around, breaking her neck in the process. Then he dropped her limp body on the ground. Other villagers, attracted by the woman's screams, gathered in the distance. They expected the enraged elephant to trample his victim. They expected him to flee at the sight of men. But he stood there, confused, dumfounded by what he had done. A superb animal, a tusker in his late twenties, shining, ten feet high at the shoulders. He switched his tail. He snorted. Then he broke a branch from a tree. But instead of eating it, he threw it on the body. He stood there for hours covering the body with leaves, branches, and torn-up knots of jungle grass, and twitching his tail. When the jungle had engulfed this evidence of guilt, the animal walked slowly away and disappeared among the sheltering trees.

Why did the elephant bury that body? So the tribesmen asked; the company's watchmen and engineers, the British planters asked, and still are asking today. Each one had a different answer, but none was satisfactory.

The tiger hides his prey from other predators to safeguard his meal for a later occasion. But the elephant had no intention of eating his victim. Why should he cover it up?

The canine covers his excrement or anything else that might betray his passage; but the elephant has no need to hide his tracks: his paths are open, his ways are free.

He felt guilty, one of the watchmen suggested. Elephants have a feeling of guilt when they kill, he said. An elephant who kills a human being becomes despondent. He isolates himself from the herd, sometimes for as long as two weeks, so one of the tribesman confirmed. An elephant will never kill a human child, another observed. Several of those present had witnessed, or had heard of, cases where an elephant had attacked and killed a grownup, or grownups, sparing the child that was with them. A wild elephant had been found playing with a baby in the garden of a nearby plantation, fondling the delighted human with his trunk and not hurting him.

What are these strange unwritten laws of the jungle? One wonders. How could a wild animal, killing a man in self-defense, develop a feeling of guilt?

Who knows? the old Indian forest officer replied. These unwritten laws, and the feeling of guilt subsequent to their violation, reflect a millennial, unique relationship between the two species, Man and Elephant.

One of the factors in this relationship may be the parallel course of their life parabolas. Man and elephant have the same prolonged childhood (even though the elephant baby is able to walk almost at once [precocial] whereas the human baby walks much later [altricial]). But nothing, except a human child, is as cuddly, plump, and cute as an elephant baby, nothing as amused and amusing as two elephant calves playfully, affectionately entwining their trunks or splashing and squealing in a river bath. In the wild, the elephant young remain long attached to mother and herd, till they are broken in completely to all the ways of the tribe. Those born in captivity are sent to "school" at the age of three or four, that is, training camps where miniature logs and tiny ropes and chains are on hand to teach them the techniques of their future trade of timber hauling. Nothing looks quite as much like a human nursery school as a well-equipped baby elephant training camp.

Sexual maturity is reached between ten and thirteen years, but childhood—the condition of emotional dependency—continues until about sixteen. Then the elephant becomes a boisterous adolescent. It is the age of flirting and fighting. Love among elephants is a touchingly sublimated affair, into which the sexual relationship enters only as a climax, so to speak. But beyond that—before, during, and after—the relationship between two young elephants who have fallen in love is one of tender, long-enduring affection and companionship. Inseparable, for periods which may last up to a year or even longer, the two will engage in games of an indescribable drollery: entwining trunks, rolling around, falling into each other's arms, rubbing heads, butting, splashing each other with water, all with a delicate clumsiness, an unshapely gracefulness hard to match anywhere in the animal kingdom. Except for these love games, however, it is difficult to see wild elephants in the act of mating. They do it discreetly, by night, apart from the others.

No one in his senses will put an elephant to work before the age of eighteen, at which point he has reached adulthood and has learned his trade, his sense of duty and responsibility. His working day is regulated like that of a human being; the span of his working life is long. In his fifties he is still full of "manhood." What a long period in which to store memories and experience. Decline and old age set in in the late fifties. Sunken-eyed, bony-cheeked, his molars worn, his tusks broken, his trunk scarred, he goes into "pension," eating a bread of charity in return for which he is asked occasionally to perform some light work, like giving tourists a morning ride through the jungle. Death may come between sixty and seventy, even though elephants are on record who have reached the exceptional age of ninety.

The training of an elephant is totally different from that of any other animal. No other wild animal, to start with, can be tamed at all after it has outgrown babyhood. The elephant on the other hand, can be domesticated in an amazingly short time even after he is fully grown up. Nor do they lose their "wild" qualities or acquire new, specifically domestic ones. Their character remains the same. The communications with the wild are not severed. Domestic elephants spend the nights roaming and grazing freely in the jungle and tame females often mate with wild males during these jungle nights.

Six weeks at various elephant training and work camps south of Madras, and I have become unreservedly one of the pro-elephant intelligence people. What I have seen convinces me that the elephant has a highly developed, complex intelligence, the limits of which we have barely begun to explore, and that the elephant perhaps better than the porpoise offers a promising approach to the study of interspecies communication.

We were out in the jungle with the rising sun, to the sounds of birds awakening. We followed the trail of the drag-chain through the high jungle grass, came across fresh droppings at one point, and after half a mile heard the lazy tintinnabulation of the elephant's bell. *"Ja, barjà"*—"come, come back"—the mahout began to chant. *"Ja, barjà, ja, barjà."* We heard underbrush crackling and breaking beneath the animal's foot. His enormous head appeared between two thickly fronded trees. Trunk down, snorting softly, still pulling up grass, Caesar walked toward us, moving his hobbled forefeet in short steps, with the melancholy grace of a Japanese lady in tiny shoes. *"Ja, barjà,"* the mahout chanted. He patted Caesar's trunk and unfastened the hobble chain. *"Allà,"* he said, *"allà, allà,"* and Caesar raised his right forefoot, which we used as a step to climb on his high withers. *"Daréi kammàt,"* the mahout ordered, "pick up your chain." Caesar obeyed at once, hanging it nonchalantly over his one huge tusk. The second tusk, the mahout explained, had been lost in an uneven combat with a wild elephant. The wild cousin had also used his advantage to nibble off a good part of Caesar's tail. One-tusked and stump-tailed, old Caesar nevertheless looked majestic, and his small eyes blinked with intelligence.

It was time for elephant bath. We rode Caesar down to the river. He tested the steep, slippery ground of the riverbank before setting down his foot. Other mahouts were already in the stream, with their elephants: tuskers and cows, and little ones playing around the cows. *"Bait, bait,"* the mahout cried out, and the beast went down on his belly and let us descend. We each took a piece of jackfruit rind—which is somewhat like dry coconut rind but rougher—and began to scrub the animal inch by inch.

"Stretch your foreleg," "raise your hindleg," "lie down on your side," "shift your trunk," "lie still," "stretch," "get up," "down on your hindlegs," "lie down on the other side," "get up," "take water in your trunk and spray your back," "spray the other side," "spray over your head," "spray your belly. . . ." This is all part of the average elephant vocabulary. The elephant understands every word of it, and performs promptly and precisely.

There has been a lot of discussion as to how much the animal really understands. Some experts say that the Indian working elephant actually performs only with his mahout on his back. He may get the general tone of the commands and exhortations, but he really obeys the impulse of the rider's leg, just like a horse, and the direction of the guiding hook the mahout always carries.

I found that this is true only to a limited extent. Elephants are trained in different ways in different parts of India. In Kerala, they are leg- and hook-conscious. One mahout said he used eighteen different signals with his feet behind the elephant's ear: left foot, right foot, toes, heels, scratch upward, scratch downward, kick, and so forth. A well-schooled elephant understands these signals without the aid of spoken commands, this mahout said. No elephant will perform without the mahout on his back, simply from the sound of spoken words. In Madras, on the other hand, elephant education is more verbal. There, the average elephant vocabulary includes from forty to sixty words, and there is no question that the elephant understands their meaning completely and accurately. Elephant language is a corrupt form of Sanskrit, passed on from mahout generation to generation, from far back in antiquity. "Speak Sanskrit to your elephant. . . ."

After the bath comes breakfast. We ride up to the camp. Women, in colorful saris, and naked children have tended to the cooking. Heavy copper kettles are hung over low fires of smoldering cow dung. In the kettles, rice and ragi—a cereal grass widely cultivated in Asia—cook and bubble. When it is done, the mixture is spread on a big wooden table to cool. Each mahout, as he arrives with his animal, cuts his share, adds some salt, and forms it into balls. Each ball weighs about three pounds. I do it for Caesar. Eight balls, the mahout tells me. Had he not told me, Caesar would have. He stands there, his trunk raised, and lets me push each ball into his gaping mouth, rolling up his tongue to hold it. When I have fed him the eighth ball, he walks away. He counted the balls as he ate them. He knew there must be eight: none less, none more.

It was almost eight o'clock. The sun was brooding on a steaming jungle, but for Caesar it was time to go to work, which, in Southern India, consists mostly of timber hauling. It requires skills as varied as the terrains on which it is done. In Kerala, jungle clearing proceeds up and down the slopes of steep mountains. The stripped logs are long and even. Some of them weigh as much as three and a half tons. At one end, a hole is drilled through the tree trunk, big enough to pass a chain through. A rope about three yards long is then knotted to the chain. *"Daréi ḳammàt,"* the mahout calls. *"Daréi ḳammàt."* The elephant picks up the rope and begins to drag the log.

The log is almost half his own weight. Two hundred yards up a steep slope. The trail has been scratched out by the passage of previous logs. Straight up. Winding between trees. Over stubborn rocks. The weight is heavy. The sun is steady and hot.

The mahout, who sits on the elephant, keeps inciting the animal with his feet, scratching and poking gently behind the ears. "Pull," he will call, "lift the thing over this rock." "Drop it." "Turn." "Walk." "Forward." "Backward." But all the details are left to the elephant's own judgment. It is he who tests the terrain, who finds the right place to set his foot. It is he who knows when to drop the rope, to push the log, to turn it. It is he who knows when he's tired, when it's time to munch a twig or chase the flies. Then he picks up the rope again and drags on.

He drags as many as thirty logs a day—an average of ninety tons —over a distance of 200 yards at an inclination of about 45 degrees. If he works seven and a half hours a day, his output can be determined to be about ten horsepower, the power of a small tractor—not counting the brain energy that the tractor lacks.

At this moment, when the whole science of animal psychology is in full revolution, particularly in the field of communication among animals and communication between man and animal— at this moment splendid experiments could be devised.

Of elephant language, little has been recorded, nothing has been analyzed. We know that elephants emit three types of sound—a hum, a whistle, and a roar. According to the Mudevan tribesmen, the humming sound indicates a warning. The whistling, they say, means that one of the herd has been injured or is otherwise in distress. The roar is a threat or signal to attack. These tribesmen probably know more than anybody else about jungle voices, but their testimony must always be taken with a grain of salt. However this may be, the "vocabulary" as they explain it sounds quite plausible and does not exceed what we would expect. On the contrary, considering the social habits of the elephant and the differentiation of his actions and reactions, we could well imagine that his vocabulary might be more varied and that elephants should be able to communicate with something approaching the precision, say, of the bees.

We do know that the elephant can "understand" our language. That he learns the sound and meaning of up to sixty words is quite common and well documented. Perhaps he can learn much more than that. One mahout claimed that his elephant understood *everything* he said, which might even be credible, when you consider that the mahout was a very simple boy whose own vocabulary probably did not exceed a few hundred words.

But we know even more. A German zoologist, Bernhard Rensch, has shown in a series of brilliant experiments that an elephant can learn to distinguish as many as twenty-six different abstract designs, among them letters of the alphabet and numbers. Not only can he learn these within the course of a few months, but he can remember them after an interval of four and a half months, so well-developed is his memory. (A young elephant at Trivandrum, Kerala, was taught a few years ago to pick up not a log, but a normal-sized piece of chalk, to walk up to the blackboard and write in a firm, legible long-trunk, "Welcome.")

We furthermore know that elephants—and other animals as well—are able to associate sound with sign. Put a rope and a chain in front of a schooled elephant; say "rope," and he will pick up and give you the rope. If you attach a sign with the word ROPE to it and one with the word CHAIN to the chain, the elephant learns quickly to associate the image of the letters with that of the object and will pick up the plaque marked CHAIN upon verbal command even if there is no longer a chain in sight.

Taken together, these capacities—the ability to learn a spoken vocabulary, to distinguish abstract designs, and to associate sound and sign—should enable the elephant to read and to write, at least in a mechanical way, on a special electric typewriter equipped with a simple superstructure containing keys about six inches in diameter.

As the first step toward learning how to "type" on such a typewriter, the animal is offered a bit of food in an open cup. After he has taken the food out of the cup several times, the cup with the food in it is covered, before his eyes, with a matching plate. The animal has to get the food by knocking away the plate.

The elephant on which I performed this experiment in the Mudumalai jungle—a four-year-old male—did not even have to "learn" this. He understood at once that it was enough to remove the plate in order to get his piece of food as before.

The next step is to mark the plate with one big black dot, for instance. When the animal has knocked away this plate twenty times or so, two cups covered with plates are offered instead of one. The one with the reward in it is marked with the familiar black dot. The other one, which is empty, is marked with two black dots. It took my elephant about ten trials to understand that he had to make a choice, that the reward was in one cup and not the other. After four work periods of twenty minutes each in four days, the elephant had acquired an 85 percent accuracy in distinguishing a green from an orange plate and one dot from two.

From dots and geometric designs one passes to words, from one and two dots one proceeds to more dots: from binary choices one moves on to multiple choices. From words, finally, one passes to letters: and from the cups and plates one eventually goes to the electric typewriter.

In a year, the elephant should be able to take simple phonetic dictation. Whether he knows what he is doing is another question. Will the animal ever be able to use the words he has learned to express needs or concepts of his own? Will he ever be able to use our language as a means to communicate with us? If he does, we'll be at a new point in animal pyschology that may open fascinating new perspectives to our understanding of nature.